Math+

2nd Edition

Activity Book

Book Staff and Contributors
Tony Freedman   *Content Specialist*
Michelle Kitt   *Director, Instructional Design for Science, Mathematics, Learning Models, and Platforms*
Jill Tunick   *Senior Text Editor*
Debra Foulks   *Text Editor*
Suzanne Montazer   *Creative Director, Print and ePublishing*
Jacquie Rosenborough   *Print Visual Designer*
Julie Jankowski   *Cover Designer*
Steve Mawyer   *Media Editor*
Carol McGehe   *Writer*
Amy Eward   *Senior Manager, Writers*
Susan Raley   *Senior Manager, Editors*
Luz Long   *Senior Project Manager*
Nols Myers   *Director K–8, Program Management*

Lynda Cloud   *Executive Vice President, Product Development*
David Pelizzari   *Vice President, K12 Content*
Kim Barcas   *Vice President, Creative*
Christopher Frescholtz   *Senior Director, Program Management*
Lisa Dimaio Iekel   *Director, Print Production and Manufacturing*

Printed By   *Quad/Graphics Versailles, Ky, USA, April, 2015*

Illustrations Credits
All illustrations © K12 Inc. unless otherwise noted
Cover: Volunteers painting a mural at Cody High School in Detroit, Michigan. © Jim West/Alamy

About K12 Inc.
K12 Inc., a technology-based education company, is the nation's leading provider of proprietary curriculum and online education programs to students in grades K–12. K12 provides its curriculum and academic services to online schools, traditional classrooms, blended school programs, and directly to families. K12 Inc. also operates the K12 International Academy, an accredited, diploma-granting online private school serving students worldwide. K12's mission is to provide any child the curriculum and tools to maximize success in life, regardless of geographic, financial, or demographic circumstances. K12 Inc. is accredited by CITA. More information can be found at www.K12.com.

ISBN: 978-1-60153-440-8   (online book)
ISBN: 978-1-60153-452-1   (printed book)

Printed by Quad/Graphics, Versailles, KY, USA, April 2016.

Contents

Fractions: Multiplication and Division

Problems Involving Fractions

Decimals: Addition and Subtraction

Decimals: Multiplication and Division

Algebra

Coordinate Planes

Perimeter, Area, and Volume

Math Reasoning: Methods and Strategies

Math Reasoning: Solutions

Data Analysis and Representation

Round Whole Numbers in Story Problems

Round Numbers in Story Problems

Reagan wants to buy a new van. The chart shows how much a new van costs at different car dealers. Use the two strategies in the table to round each price.

	Car dealer	Friendly numbers	Nearest thousand
1.	Car Dealer A $39,528	?	?
2.	Car Dealer B $36,102	?	?
3.	Car Dealer C $38,999	?	?

4. Reagan wants to be sure he has enough money to buy the van from Car Dealer A. Which rounded number should Reagan use to estimate the amount of money he needs? Explain.

Round the numbers as directed.

5. In 1987, professional football player Walter Payton set a new record for career rushing yards. His record was 16,726 rushing yards. Round Payton's record to the nearest hundred yards.

6. The Empire State Building in New York City cost $24,718,000 to build in 1931. Round the total cost to the nearest million dollars.

7. In 2005 there were 3,844,829 people living in Los Angeles. Round the population to the nearest ten thousand.

8. The total cost of building the Washington Monument was $1,187,710. Round the total cost to the nearest ten thousand dollars.

9. The total number of people attending professional football games for the 2007 regular season was 17,341,012. Round the total attendance to the nearest hundred thousand.

TRY IT

Choose the answer.

10. Last month the earth was about 91,348,000 miles from the sun. Which answer choice shows this distance rounded to the nearest ten million miles?

A. 90,000,000 mi

B. 91,000,000 mi

C. 91,300,000 mi

D. 91,400,000 mi

11. The distance between Sydney, Australia, and Paris, France, is 16,968 kilometers. Which answer choice shows this distance rounded to the nearest thousand kilometers?

A. 14,000 km

B. 15,000 km

C. 16,000 km

D. 17,000 km

12. The number of Americans who use text messaging is estimated to be more than 83,780,000. Which answer choice shows this number rounded to the nearest million?

A. 80,000,000

B. 83,000,000

C. 84,000,000

D. 90,000,000

13. The newspaper reported that the attendance at Yankee Stadium II in New York City in 2005 was 4,100,000 when rounded to the nearest hundred thousand people. Which could have been the exact attendance in 2005?

A. 4,017,598

B. 4,045,962

C. 4,090,696

D. 4,152,067

14. The height of Mount Chimborazo in Ecuador is 21,000 feet above sea level when rounded to the nearest thousand. But the height is 20,600 feet when rounded to the nearest hundred. Which could be the exact height of Mount Chimborazo?

A. 20,458 ft

B. 20,561 ft

C. 20,672 ft

D. 21,432 ft

TRY IT

Estimate and Find Sums and Differences

Estimate and Solve

Use clustering to estimate the sum. Choose the answer.

1. $377 + 386 + 372 + 389 = ?$

   A. 400

   B. 1,000

   C. 1,600

2. $43 + 32 + 44 + 35 = ?$

   A. 160

   B. 120

   C. 200

Round to friendly numbers that are multiples of 100 to estimate. Choose the answer.

3. $9,629 + 8,573 = ?$

   A. 17,000

   B. 18,200

   C. 19,200

4. $76,999 - 68,205 = ?$

   A. 6,000

   B. 7,200

   C. 8,800

Estimate by rounding the numbers to the nearest ten thousand.
Choose the answer.

5. $56,880 + 43,375 = ?$

   A. 90,000

   B. 100,000

   C. 110,000

6. $325,686 - 124,478 = ?$

   A. 200,000

   B. 210,000

   C. 250,000

Complete the table. Estimate each sum or difference by using one of the strategies above. Then find the exact answer. Decide if the estimate is reasonable.

	Problem	Estimate	Exact answer
7.	$2,134 + 7,322 = ?$	?	?
8.	$34,672 - 13,440 = ?$	?	?

Estimate by first rounding the numbers to the nearest hundred thousand. Then find the exact answer. Are your estimate and exact answer close?

9. $8,925,181 + 2,820,084$

10. $8,189,378 - 5,428,310$

T R Y   I T

Estimate Sums and Differences (A)

Estimate Story Problems

Read the problem and follow the directions.

1. The Mississippi National River and Recreation Area provides food and shelter to about 50 species of mammals, 270 species of birds, 150 species of fish, and 25 species of mussels. About how many species are helped in all? Round each addend by using a friendly number that is a multiple of 25. Show your work.

2. For Problem 1, find the exact answer. Show your work.

3. In 2007, the national parks had 3,003,270 overnight visitors in tents and 5,110,811 overnight visitors in recreational vehicles. Round the addends to the nearest million. Estimate about how many overnight visitors in tents and overnight visitors in recreational vehicles there were altogether. Show your work.

4. For Problem 3, find the exact answer. Show your work.

For Problems 5–8, use a rounding strategy to round the addends. Estimate the sum and then solve the story problem.

5. The Kelly family bought a car and a van. They paid $23,956 for the car and $28,412 for the van. How much did the family spend on the two vehicles? Was your estimate close to your exact answer?

6. A website had more than 41,252,000 visitors in 2005. In 2006, there were 12,452,000 visitors. What was the total number of visitors for the two years? Was your estimate close to your exact answer?

7. In 2007, Los Angeles had a population of 3,834,340 and San Diego had a population of 1,266,731. What was the total population of Los Angeles and San Diego? Was your estimate close to your exact answer?

8. In the election for city mayor, the winner received 76,262 votes, and the other person running received 73,672 votes. How many total votes were cast? Was your estimate close to your exact answer?

Choose the answer.

9. A large bin held 56,360 marbles. A small bin held 17,580 marbles. Find the exact answer. How many marbles were in both bins?

   A. 38,780   B. 63,940   C. 73,940   D. 74,940

TRY IT

Estimate Sums and Differences (B)

Practice Estimating with Subtraction

Solve. Show your work.

1. British astronomer William Herschel discovered the planet Uranus in 1781. In the year 2015, how long will it have been, rounded to the nearest hundred years, since Uranus was discovered?

2. For Problem 1, find the exact difference.

3. Satellite orbits vary in their distance from the earth. Orbits can be anywhere from 252,800 to 35,200,000 yards. What is the greatest distance between satellite orbits? Round to the nearest ten thousand yards to estimate.

4. For Problem 3, find the exact difference.

Use a rounding strategy to round the numbers. Estimate the difference. Then find the exact answer. Explain whether your estimate was reasonable.

5. Last year the local newspaper printed 931,244 newspapers. This year it printed only 310,201 newspapers. How many fewer newspapers did it print this year?

6. Sofia's mom traveled 78,109 miles for work two years ago. Last year she traveled 21,311 miles. How many more miles did she travel two years ago than last year?

Choose the answer.

7. During last year's baseball season, 52,462 people attended the local team's home games. This year, only 33,200 people attended the home games. If you round each number to the nearest ten thousand, what is the estimated difference between the attendance in the two years?

   A. 9,000   B. 19,000   C. 20,000   D. 21,000

8. When the Smiths bought their house, they paid $480,400. Several years later, the price rose to $590,500. How much more is the house worth now than when they bought it? Find the exact answer.

   A. $111,000   B. $110,100   C. $101,100   D. $100,110

T R Y   I T

Place-Value Patterns

Patterns in Place Values

You can find patterns by comparing place values.

PROBLEM 1 Compare the place value of the digit 4 in the thousands place with the place value of the digit 4 in the hundreds place in the number 4,444.

SOLUTION

1 Write 4,444 in expanded form. To write the number in expanded form is to write it out as a sum, using the digits in the number and their place values. In 4,444, moving from left to right, the first 4 is in the thousands place, the second 4 is in the hundreds place, the third 4 is in the tens place, and the last 4 is in the ones place. Here is the expanded form:

$$4,444 = 4 \times 1,000 + 4 \times 100 + 4 \times 10 + 4 \times 1$$

2 Compare the place value of the 4 in the thousands place with the place value of the 4 in the hundreds place. Since 1 thousand is equivalent to 10 hundreds, 10 times a hundred is 1 thousand. In other words, the thousands place is 10 times as great as the hundreds place.

ANSWER The 4 in the thousands place is 10 times as great as the 4 in the hundreds place.

You can also see this relationship in a place-value chart.

Thousands						
100,000	10,000	1,000		100	10	1
hundred thousands	ten thousands	thousands		hundreds	tens	ones
		4	**,**	**4**	**4**	**4**

You can write the values for each of the places over the words in the chart, as shown. Choose any two digits that are one place value apart in the number 4,444. You can see that the digit to the left is always 10 times as great as the digit to the right.

L E A R N

PROBLEM 2 Compare the place value of the digit 7 in the thousands place with the place value of the digit 7 in the ten thousands place in the number 77,777.

1 Write 77,777 in expanded form.

$77,777 = 7 \times 10,000 + 7 \times 1,000 + 7 \times 100 + 7 \times 10 + 7 \times 1.$

2 Compare the place value of the 7 in the thousands place with the place value of the 7 in the ten thousands place. Once again, you can use a place-value chart with the place values labeled with numbers, as shown.

Thousands				100	10	1
100,000	10,000	1,000				
hundred thousands	ten thousands	thousands		hundreds	tens	ones
	7	7	,	7	7	7

Since 10 thousands is equivalent to 10 thousand, you can say that a thousand is $\frac{1}{10}$ as great as 10 thousand.

ANSWER The 7 in the thousands place is $\frac{1}{10}$ as great as the 7 in the ten thousands place.

You can try other examples to see the general pattern at work:

Choose any two digits that are one place value apart in the number 77,777. You can see that the digit to the right is always $\frac{1}{10}$ as great as the digit to its left.

Compare the place values in each problem for the number 222,222.

1. the 2 in the ones place with the 2 in the tens place

2. the 2 in the thousands place with the 2 in the hundreds place

3. the 2 in the ten thousands place with the 2 in the hundred thousands place

Compare the place values in each problem for the number 555,555,555.

4. the 5 in the hundred thousands place with the 5 in the millions place

5. the 5 in the hundred thousands place with the 5 in the ten thousands place

LEARN

Bases and Exponents (A)

Evaluate Expressions

Read the problem and follow the directions.

1. Write 36^2 using repeated multiplication.

2. Draw a sketch to show 6^2.

3. Find the value of 36^2.

4. Write 5^3 using repeated multiplication.

5. Write $27 \times 27 \times 27$ as a single base with an exponent.

6. Write $77 \cdot 77$ as a single base with an exponent.

7. Write 8^3 using repeated multiplication, and then compute the value.

8. Write 7^2 using repeated multiplication, and then compute the value.

Write the base and exponent for the expression.

9.

Exponent form	14^2
Base	?
Exponent	?

10.

Exponent form	20^3
Base	?
Exponent	?

Choose the answer.

11. What is another way to write 43^3?

   A. $3 \cdot 43$ B. $43 \cdot 43 \cdot 43$ C. $3 \cdot 4 \cdot 3$ D. $3 \cdot 3 \cdot 3$

12. Which expression shows $24 \cdot 24$ written as a base and an exponent?

   A. 224 B. $24 \cdot 2$ C. 24^2 D. $2 \cdot 24$

TRY IT

13. Which expression shows 68^2 by using repeated multiplication?

A. $68 \cdot 2$ 　　　 B. $2 \cdot 2$ 　　　 C. $6 \cdot 8 \cdot 2$ 　　　 D. $68 \cdot 68$

14. Which model shows 7^2?

A.

B.

C.

D.

15. Which model shows 4^3?

A.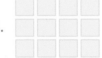

B.

C.

D.

TRY IT

Bases and Exponents (B)

Work with Exponents of 4 and 5

Read the problem and follow the directions.

1. Write 5^4 using multiple factors.

2. Write 17^5 using multiple factors.

3. Write 8^4 using multiple factors, and then compute the value.

4. Write 4^5 using multiple factors, and then compute the value.

5. Write $33 \cdot 33 \cdot 33 \cdot 33$ as a single base with an exponent.

Write the base and exponent for the expression.

6.

Exponent form	23^5
Base	?
Exponent	?

7.

Exponent form	18^5
Base	?
Exponent	?

Choose the answer.

8. What is another way to write 26^4?

   A. $26 \cdot 26 \cdot 26 \cdot 26$

   B. $26 \cdot 4$

   C. $2 \cdot 6 \cdot 4$

   D. $26 \cdot 26 \cdot 26 \cdot 26 \cdot 26$

9. Which shows a true statement?

   A. $5^4 > 4^5$

   B. $5^4 < 4^5$

   C. $5^4 = 4^5$

   D. $5^4 + 4^5 = 54$

10. Which shows $12 \cdot 12 \cdot 12 \cdot 12 \cdot 12$ written as a single base with an exponent?

    A. 5^{12} 　　　　　　 B. 12^{12} 　　　　　　 C. 12^5

11. Compare 13^4 and $13 \cdot 13 \cdot 13$. Which statement is true?

    A. $13^4 < 13 \cdot 13 \cdot 13$ 　　 B. $13^4 = 13 \cdot 13 \cdot 13$ 　　 C. $13^4 > 13 \cdot 13 \cdot 13$

12. Compare 4^3 and 3^4. Which statement is true?

    A. $4^3 < 3^4$ 　　　　　 B. $4^3 = 3^4$ 　　　　　 C. $4^3 > 3^4$

Solve.

1. The Children's Theater can seat 1,575 people in 63 equal rows. The Bartell Theater can seat 2,048 people in 64 equal rows. How many more or fewer people are seated in each row at the Bartell Theater than at the Children's Theater, if all the seats are filled at both theaters?

   (a) Draw a diagram to represent the problem.

   (b) Solve the problem. Explain how you found your answer.

2. Jake and Lacy work at a golf driving range. At the end of the day, Jake collected 408 golf balls and Lacy collected 374 golf balls. They need to put them into baskets with 34 golf balls in each basket. How many baskets will Jake and Lacy fill altogether?

   (a) Use equations to represent the problem. Solve the problem and explain your thinking.

   (b) Use equations to represent another way to solve the problem. Solve the problem this different way and explain your thinking.

3. Maddy has a dog walking business. She charges $6.75 per hour to walk 1 dog and $10.50 per hour to walk 2 dogs. Maddy can walk up to 4 dogs at a time. How much will Maddy make if she walks Chloe's 2 dogs and Deon's 1 dog for a total of 2 hours?

   (a) What operations can be used to solve the problem? How do you know?

   (b) Explain and solve the problem in two different ways.

4. Izzie multiplied 436×203. She said the partial products she used to solve the problem are 1,308 and 87,200. Do you agree? Explain your answer.

T R Y I T

5. State the actions and thinking you used during this lesson as a math learner.

Math Thinking and Actions
I made sense of problems by • Explaining to myself what a problem means and what it asks for • Using drawings or diagrams to represent a problem I was solving
I explained my math thinking clearly.
I tried out new ways to check if an answer is reasonable.
Other

TRY IT

Angles (A)

Measure Angles

Use a protractor to measure the angle. Write the angle measure.

1.

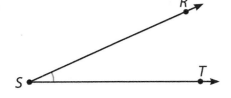

2.

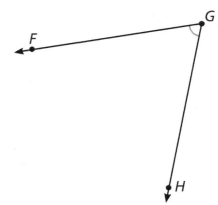

3.

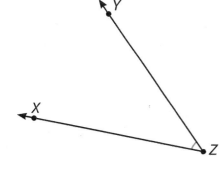

4.

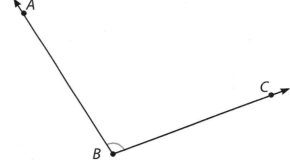

5.

T R Y   I T

6.

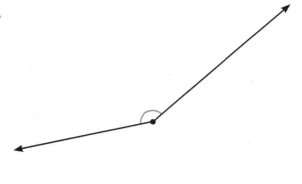

7.

Draw the given angle.

8. obtuse angle

9. acute angle

10. straight angle

11. 90° angle
Name the angle as either an acute angle, an obtuse angle, a right angle, or a straight angle.

Choose the answer.

12. Classify this angle.

    A. acute
    B. obtuse
    C. right
    D. straight

13. Classify this angle.

    A. acute
    B. obtuse
    C. right
    D. straight

14. Which is an obtuse angle?

    A.

    B.

    C.

    D.

T R Y   I T

Angles (B)

Draw and Measure Angles

Use a protractor to measure the angle. Record the measures and describe the angle as acute, right, obtuse, or straight.

1.

2.

3.

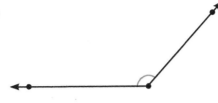

4.

Use a ruler and a protractor to draw the angle to the given measure. Describe the angle as acute, right, obtuse, or straight.

5. 110°

6. 35°

7. 90°

8. Draw a straight angle, label the center *B*, and show the angle measure.

9. Draw a 45° angle.

10. Draw a 120° angle.

11. Draw a 160° angle.

12. Draw a 180° angle.

T R Y   I T

Perpendicular and Parallel Lines

Practice Types of Lines

Answer the question and draw lines as directed.

1. What are perpendicular lines?

2. Give one example of perpendicular lines that you see around you every day.

3. Construct perpendicular lines using a compass and ruler.

4. What are intersecting lines?

5. Give one example of intersecting lines that you see around you every day.

6. Draw intersecting lines.

7. What are parallel lines?

8. Give one example of parallel lines that you see around you every day.

9. Construct parallel lines, using a compass and a ruler.

Choose the answer.

10. Identify these lines.

    A. parallel

    B. perpendicular

    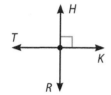

11. Identify lines *EF* and *GH*.

    A. parallel

    B. perpendicular

    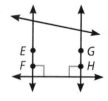

T R Y   I T

Identify and Classify Triangles

Classify Triangles

Solve.

1. What is the name of a triangle that has only 2 of its 3 sides the same length?

2. How is an acute triangle different from both an obtuse triangle and a right triangle?

Name the triangle by its angles and its side lengths.

3.
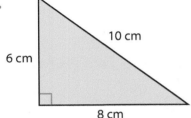
10 cm

6 cm

8 cm

4.
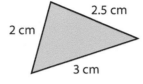
2.5 cm

2 cm

3 cm

5.
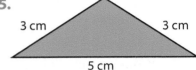
3 cm   3 cm

5 cm

Draw.

6. Use a ruler and an index card to draw an obtuse scalene triangle.

7. Use a ruler to draw an equilateral triangle.

8. Use a ruler to draw an acute isosceles triangle.

Choose the answer.

9. Which best describes an equilateral triangle?

   A. All sides are the same length; all angles have the same measure.

   B. Two sides are the same length; one angle measures 90°.

   C. Two sides are the same length; all angles measure less than 90°.

   D. Two sides are the same length; one angle measures greater than 90°.

10. Which best describes a right isosceles triangle?

   A. Two sides are the same length; one angle measures 90°.

   B. All sides are the same length; two angles measure 90°.

   C. All sides are different lengths; one angle measures 90°.

   D. Two sides are the same length; one angle measures greater than 90°.

TRY IT

11. Which triangle always has 1 right angle and 2 sides the same length?

    A. acute isosceles

    B. right isosceles

    C. right equilateral

    D. acute scalene

12. Which triangle always has all sides different lengths and all angles measuring less than 90°?

    A. obtuse equilateral

    B. acute scalene

    C. equilateral

    D. obtuse isosceles

13. Which seems to best describe this triangle?

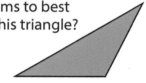

    A. All sides are the same length; all angles are the same.

    B. Two sides are the same length; one angle measures 90°.

    C. Two sides are the same length; all angles are less than 90°.

    D. Two sides are the same length; one angle is obtuse.

14. Which appears to be an equilateral triangle?

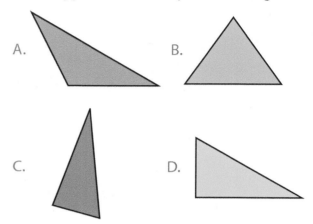

15. Which name correctly classifies this triangle?

3 in.   3 in.

2.5 in.

    A. acute isosceles

    B. obtuse equilateral

    C. acute scalene

    D. obtuse isosceles

16. Which name correctly classifies this triangle?

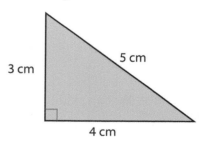

3 cm   5 cm

4 cm

    A. right isosceles

    B. obtuse equilateral

    C. acute scalene

    D. right scalene

TRY IT

Answer the question.

1. How are these two shapes alike and how are they different?

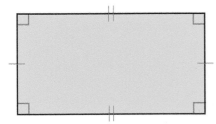 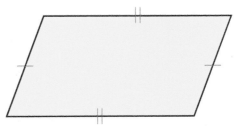

2. How are these two shapes alike and how are they different?

Read the problem and follow the directions.

3. Use a ruler to draw a parallelogram and a trapezoid. Explain how these two shapes are alike and how they are different.

4. Use a ruler to draw a rectangle and a square. Explain how these two shapes are alike and how they are different.

Choose the answer.

5. Which shape has one pair of opposite sides that are parallel but not equal in length?

   A. parallelogram

   B. square

   C. trapezoid

   D. rhombus

6. Which statement is true for all rectangles?

   A. All sides are equal in length.

   B. All angles are right angles.

   C. All angles are acute.

   D. Two angles are obtuse and two angles are acute.

TRY IT

7. Which best describes this quadrilateral?

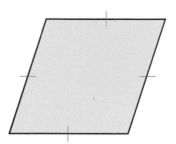

A. polygon with all right angles

B. polygon with exactly one pair of sides that are equal in length

C. polygon with exactly one pair of parallel sides

D. polygon with four sides that are equal in length

8. Which shape has opposite sides that are both equal in length and parallel?

A. triangle

B. trapezoid

C. pentagon

D. parallelogram

9. Which shape has 4 congruent sides?

A. circle

B. trapezoid

C. rhombus

D. triangle

10. Choose **all** the names that could be used to classify this shape.

A. quadrilateral

B. trapezoid

C. parallelogram

D. rectangle

11. Choose **all** the names that could be used to classify this shape.

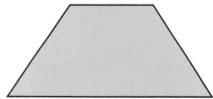

A. rhombus

B. parallelogram

C. quadrilateral

D. trapezoid

TRY IT

Identify and Classify Quadrilaterals (C)

Identify and Classify Quadrilaterals

Describe the characteristics the figures have in common.

1.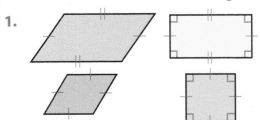

2.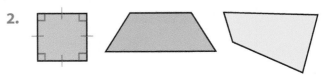

Choose the answer.

3. I have 4 sides. What shape am I?

   A. pentagon

   B. quadrilateral

   C. hexagon

   D. octagon

4. I have 4 sides and 1 pair of parallel lines. What shape am I?

   A. parallelogram

   B. square

   C. rhombus

   D. trapezoid

5. I have two 2 pairs of parallel sides. My side lengths are all equal. I have no right angles. What shape am I?

   A. rectangle

   B. septagon

   C. square

   D. rhombus

Explain your answer.

6. Do you agree or disagree with the following statement? Explain your answer.

   "All rectangles have 4 right angles and squares have 4 right angles, so all squares are rectangles."

7. Sketch the order of quadrilaterals from least specialized to most specialized.

TRY IT

Construct Triangles and Quadrilaterals

Construct Each Shape

Worked Examples

You can construct and draw perpendicular lines.

PROBLEM Draw a line perpendicular to line segment *AB*.

SOLUTION

1 Draw a line segment about 3 inches long. Label the endpoints *A* and *B*.

2 Set the point of the compass at point *A*. Open the compass a width that is not all the way to point *B*, but beyond the middle of the line segment. Draw an arc that extends from above the middle of the line segment to below the middle of the line segment.

3 Leave the compass the same width and set the point of the compass at point *B*. Draw a second arc that crosses the first arc both above and below the line segment. Label the point where the arcs cross above the line segment as point *C* and the point where the arcs cross below the line segment as point *D*.

4 Use a ruler to draw line *CD*, which will be perpendicular to line segment *AB*. Label the point where line *CD* and line segment *AB* intersect as point *E*.

5 Use a protractor to measure angles *CEA* and *CEB*. Check that each angle measures exactly 90°. Angles *DEA* and *DEB* will also measure exactly 90°.

ANSWER

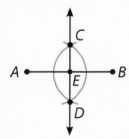

LEARN

Follow the step-by-step directions to construct the shape.

1. equilateral triangle

   STEP **1** Draw line segment *JK*.

   J •————————————• K

   STEP **2** Place the point of the compass on point *J* and the pencil at point *K*. Draw an arc with the center at point *J* and radius *JK* that extends above the line segment.

   STEP **3** Without changing the size of the compass opening, draw an arc with center at point *K* that intersects the first arc.

   STEP **4** Label the point where the arcs intersect point *L*.

   STEP **5** Draw line segments that connect point *L* to point *J* and point *L* to point *K*. Triangle *JLK* is equilateral.

2. square

   STEP **1** Draw line segment *OP*.

   O •————————————• P

   STEP **2** Place the point of the compass on point *O* and the pencil at point *P*. Draw an arc with the center at point *O* and radius *OP* that extends above and below the line segment.

   STEP **3** Without changing the size of the compass opening, draw an arc with center at point *P* that intersects the first arc at two points. Label one point *Q* and one point *R*.

   STEP **4** Draw the line segment that connects points *Q* and *R*. Label the line segment *n* and the intersection of this line segment with line segment *OP* as point *S*.

   STEP **5** Draw a circle with center at point *S* and radius *SP*.

   STEP **6** The circle will intersect with line segment *n* at two points. Label these points *T* and *U*.

   STEP **7** Draw line segments *OT*, *TP*, *PU*, and *UO*. The resulting figure is a square.

3. right triangle

   STEP **1** Draw a line segment and mark point *A* on the line segment.

   •————————•————————•
                     A

   STEP **2** Place the point of the compass on point *A*. Draw an arc on the right end of the line segment from point *A*. Label the intersection point *B*.

LEARN

3 Leave the compass the same width and place the point of the compass on point *A*. Draw a second arc on the left end of the line segment from point *A* and label this point *C*.

4 Open the compass a little more and set the point of the compass on point *B*. Draw an arc over point *A* above the line segment.

5 Leave the compass the same width and set the point of the compass on point *C*. Draw an arc over point *A* above the line segment.

6 Mark the point where the arcs meet point *D*.

7 Use a ruler to draw perpendicular line segment *AD*.

8 Use a ruler to draw line segment *DB*. Triangle *DAB* is a right triangle.

4. rectangle

1 Draw line segment *AB*.

A •————————————————• B

2 Place the point of the compass on point *A* and the pencil at point *B*. Draw an arc with the center at point *A* and radius *AB* that extends above and below the line segment.

3 Leave the compass the same width and draw an arc with center at point *B* that intersects the first arc at two points. Label these two points of intersection *C* and *D*.

4 Draw the line segment that connects points *C* and *D*. Label the line segment *e* and the intersection of this line segment with line segment *AB* as point *F*.

5 Draw a circle with center at point *F* and radius *FB*.

6 The circle will intersect with line segment *e* at two points. Label these points *G* and *H*.

7 Draw line segments *AG*, *GB*, *BH*, and *HA*. The resulting figure is a square.

8 Use a ruler to extend line segment *AG*. Mark point *I* at the end of line segment *AG*.

9 Use a ruler to extend line segment *HB*. Make sure to extend line segment *HB* so that it is the same length as line segment *AI*. Mark point *J*.

10 Use a ruler to connect points *I* and *J*. The resulting figure is a rectangle.

Construct Triangles and Quadrilaterals

Practice Triangles and Quadrilaterals

Draw the shape.

1. square

2. rectangle

3. equilateral triangle

4. right triangle

Use a compass and ruler to construct the shape.

5. right triangle

6. rectangle

TRY IT

Angles and Triangles (A)

Measure Angles in Triangles

You can use a protractor to measure angles in a triangle.

PROBLEM Review how to use a protractor to measure angle *FGH*.

SOLUTION

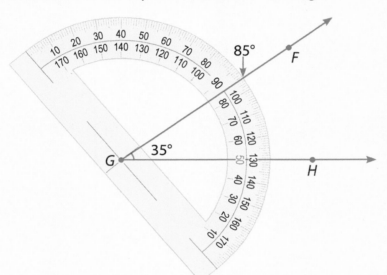

1 Place the center of the protractor on the vertex of the angle. Have one of the angle's rays pass through a friendly degree measure on the inner scale. A friendly degree measure is a number on the protractor's scale that makes it easy for you to use mental math to add and subtract.

2 Use 50° as a friendly degree measure. You could choose a different friendly degree measure, but you should always get the same results.

3 Note where the other angle's ray is passing through the protractor. Subtract the lesser measure on the protractor's scale, 50°, from the greater measure, 85°, to find the angle's measure.

4 85 − 50 = 35

ANSWER Angle *FGH* measures 35°.

Use these steps to measure the triangle's three angles. Then add the angle measures. The sum of the angle measures should be 180°.

Use a protractor to measure the angles in the triangle. Then find the sum of the angle measures. Classify the triangle as acute, right, obtuse, or equiangular.

1.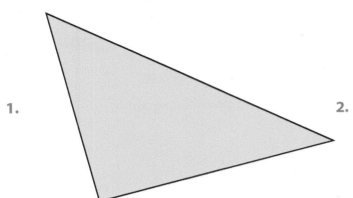

2.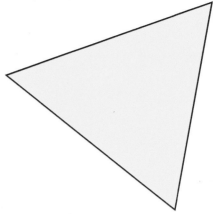

3.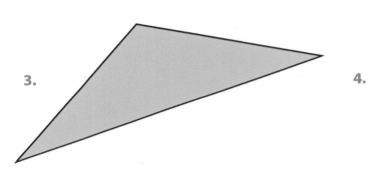

4.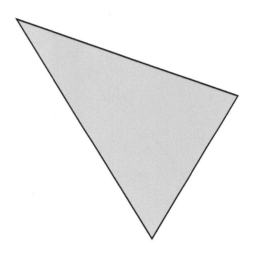

5.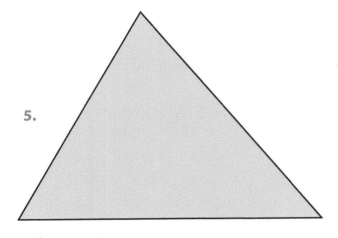

6.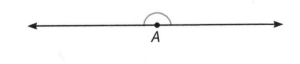

A

LEARN

Angles and Triangles (B)

Find Missing Angle Measures

The sum of the angle measures of any triangle is 180°. Find the missing angle measure in the triangle.

1.
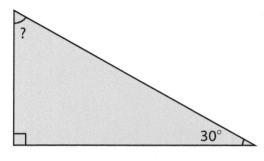

2.
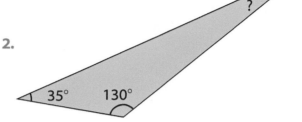

3.
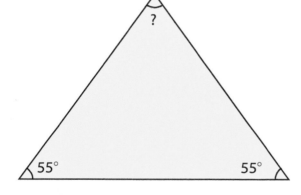

4.
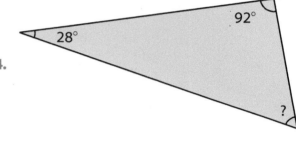

5.
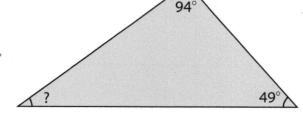

T R Y I T

Read the problem and follow the directions.

6. Claire was asked to draw a triangle with 3 angles measuring 15°, 15°, and 160°. Will she be able to draw a triangle with these angle measures?

   Explain your answer.

7. Alyssa was asked to draw a triangle with 3 angles measuring 42°, 68°, and 70°. Will she be able to draw a triangle with these angle measures?

   Explain your answer.

8. Jaime was asked to draw a triangle with 3 angles measuring 77°, 23°, and 79°. Will he be able to draw a triangle with these angle measures?

   Explain your answer.

9. Jacob made a triangular pennant for a football game. One angle measure is 40°. Another angle measure is 70°. What is the measure of the third angle?

10. The sign over the entrance to a tree house is the shape of a triangle. The measures of the angles of the triangle are equal. What is the measure of each angle?

11. One angle of a right triangle is 40°. What is the measure of each of the other 2 angles?

12. Angles K and M of triangle KLM each measure 35°. What is the measure of angle L?

Choose the answer.

13. What is the measure of ∠Y?

    A. 8°
    B. 12°
    C. 88°
    D. 92°

    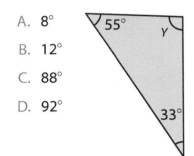

14. What is the measure of ∠L?

    A. 53°
    B. 89°
    C. 91°
    D. 119°

    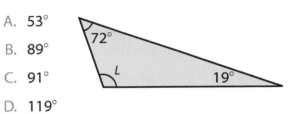

15. What is the measure of ∠R?

    A. 41°
    B. 49°
    C. 82°
    D. 98°

    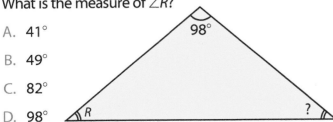

TRY IT

Angles in a Quadrilateral (A)

Measure Angles

Worked Examples

You can use a protractor to measure angles in a quadrilateral.

PROBLEM Review how to use a protractor to measure angle *FGH*.

SOLUTION

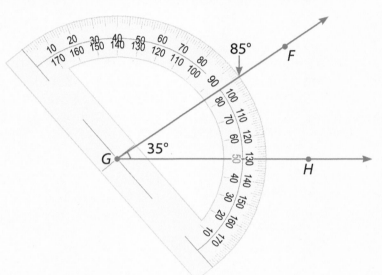

1. Place the center of the protractor on the vertex of the angle. Have one of the angle's rays pass through a friendly degree measure on the inner scale. A friendly degree measure is a number on the protractor's scale that makes it easy for you to use mental math to add and subtract.

2. Use 50° as a friendly degree measure. You could choose a different friendly degree measure, but you should always get the same results.

3. Note where the other angle's ray is passing through the protractor. Subtract the lesser measure on the protractor's scale, 50°, from the greater measure, 85°, to find the angle's measure.

4. $85 - 50 = 35$

ANSWER Angle *FGH* measures 35°.

Use these steps to measure the quadrilateral's four angles. Then add the angle measures. The sum of the angle measures should be 360°.

Use a protractor to measure the angles in the quadrilateral. Then find the sum of the angle measures and write the name of the quadrilateral.

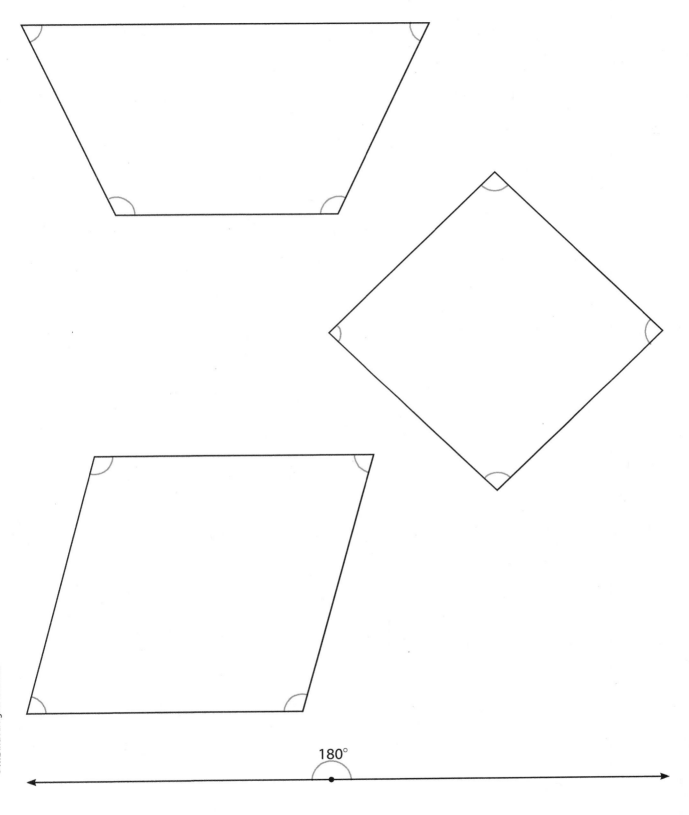

180°

31

LEARN

Measure each angle on the quadrilateral. Use a protractor or angle ruler.
Then find the sum of the angle measures.

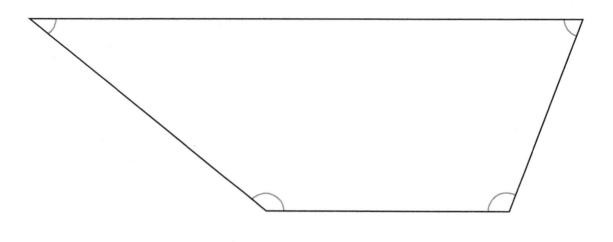

180°

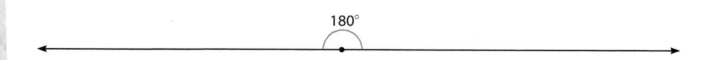

LEARN

Angles in a Quadrilateral (B)

Practice Quadrilateral Angles

Solve.

1. A quadrilateral has angles that measure 77°, 108°, and 65°. What is the measure of the fourth angle?

2. A quadrilateral has angles that measure 91°, 96°, and 88°. What is the measure of the fourth angle?

3. A quadrilateral has angles that measure 87°, 69°, and 104°. What is the measure of the fourth angle?

4. What is the measure of angle *K*?

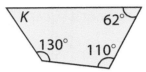

5. What is the measure of ∠*B*?

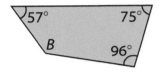

6. What is the measure of ∠*S*?

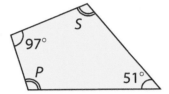

7. What is the measure of ∠*E*?

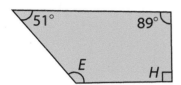

Choose the answer.

8. What is the measure of ∠*C*?

   A. 83°   B. 93°

   C. 103°   D. 123°

9. What is the measure of ∠*G*?

   A. 68°   B. 78°

   C. 88°   D. 98°

10. What is the measure of ∠*F*?

    A. 97°   B. 101°

    C. 111°   D. 121°

TRY IT

Solve.

1. Draw each of the figures described.

   (a) a parallelogram that is not a rectangle or rhombus

   (b) a scalene right triangle

   (c) an isosceles obtuse triangle

   (d) a rhombus that is not a square

   (e) a trapezoid

2. Create the quadrilateral hierarchy with these shapes: rectangle, trapezoid, parallelogram, quadrilateral, square, and rhombus.

3. Determine whether each statement is true or false.

   (a) A parallelogram always has 2 pairs of parallel sides.

   (b) An equilateral triangle has 3 equal angles.

   (c) All rhombuses are parallelograms.

   (d) A scalene triangle has no equal sides.

   (e) A square has the characteristics of both a rectangle and a rhombus.

   (f) All the angles of a rhombus must have equal measures.

   (g) The square is the most specialized quadrilateral.

   (h) An isosceles triangle is a special type of equilateral triangle.

   (i) A trapezoid is not a parallelogram.

4. Which is the best definition for a rhombus?

   A. a quadrilateral with 4 equal sides

   B. a parallelogram with 4 equal sides

   C. a parallelogram with 4 equal angles

   D. a quadrilateral with 4 equal sides and 4 equal angles

TRY IT

5. State the actions and thinking you used during this lesson as a math learner.

Math Thinking and Actions

I made sense of problems by
  • Explaining to myself what a problem means and what it asks for
  • Using drawings or diagrams to represent a problem I was solving

I explained my math thinking clearly.
I tried out new ways to check if an answer is reasonable.
Other

TRY IT

Unit Review

Checkpoint Practice

Solve.

1. Which is an obtuse angle?

A.  15°

B.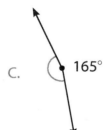

C. 165°

D. 180°

Use a protractor to find the measure of the angle.

2.

A. 50°
B. 120°
C. 130°
D. 150°

3.

A. 20°
B. 30°
C. 150°
D. 160°

4.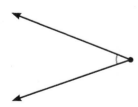

A. 42°
B. 52°
C. 132°
D. 142°

5.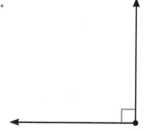

A. 70°
B. 80°
C. 90°
D. 180°

UNIT REVIEW

Choose the answer.

6. Look at the blue lines in each picture. Which pair is an example of parallel lines?

A.

B.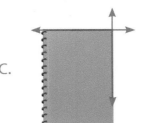

C.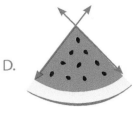

D.

7. Which is an example of perpendicular lines?

A.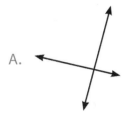

B.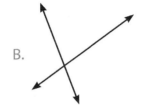

C.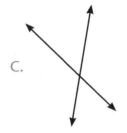

D.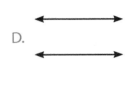

8. Identify these lines.

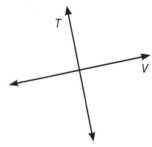

A. parallel   B. perpendicular

9. Look at the blue line segments in the picture. Identify the line segments.

A. perpendicular   B. parallel

Draw the following figures. Use marks to show right angles and equal sides as needed.

10. right isosceles triangle

11. obtuse scalene triangle

12. equilateral triangle

UNIT REVIEW

13. trapezoid

14. rectangle

15. rhombus

16. quadrilateral

Which category of two-dimensional shapes applies to all three of these shapes?

17.

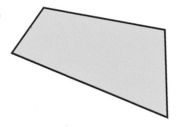 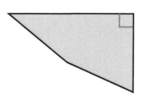 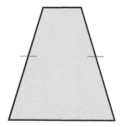

A. trapezoid	B. parallelogram
C. quadrilateral	D. rhombus

Choose the answer.

18. Which is the best definition for a rhombus?

   A. a quadrilateral with 1 right angle

   B. a quadrilateral with 2 pairs of parallel sides

   C. a parallelogram with 4 equal sides

   D. a square with no right angles

19. Which is the best definition for a square?

   A. a parallelogram with 4 right angles and 4 equal sides

   B. a parallelogram with 4 equal sides

   C. a quadrilateral with no parallel sides

   D. a rectangle with 1 pair of parallel sides

Choose all answers that are correct.

20. Which statements are true?

   A. All 4-sided shapes are either parallelograms or trapezoids.

   B. All squares are rhombuses.

   C. Some parallelograms are rectangles.

   D. Some squares are rectangles.

21. Which names can be used to classify this triangle?

   A. obtuse

   B. acute

   C. equilateral

   D. scalene

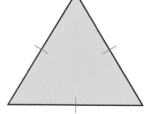

22. A triangle has angles that measure 57° and 44°. What is the measure of the third angle?

A. 13°

B. 79°

C. 99°

D. 101°

23. A triangle has angles that measure 11° and 88°. What is the measure of the third angle?

A. 12°

B. 79°

C. 81°

D. 98°

24. What is the measure of ∠M?

A. 42°

B. 90°

C. 138°

D. 180°

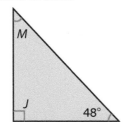

25. What is the measure of ∠D?

A. 25°

B. 65°

C. 115°

D. 155°

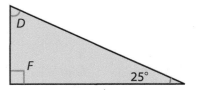

26. What is the measure of ∠R?

A. 13°

B. 52°

C. 76°

D. 104°

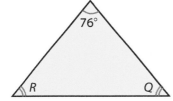

27. What is the measure of ∠F?

A. 66°

B. 76°

C. 106°

D. 116°

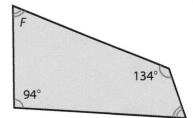

Fraction Multiplication (A)

Multiplying Fractions

1. Use the given number line to solve each problem and explain your thinking. Simplify fractions first, if needed.

   (a) $\frac{4}{5} \times 15 = \underline{\ ?\ }$

   (b) $\frac{9}{12} \times 20 = \underline{\ ?\ }$

2. Use the given array to solve each problem and explain your thinking. Simplify fractions first, if needed.

   (a) $\frac{8}{12} \times 18 = \underline{\ ?\ }$

   (b) $\frac{3}{8} \times 16 = \underline{\ ?\ }$

   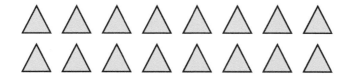

TRY IT

3. Use fraction strips to solve the problem and explain your thinking.

   $6 \times \frac{2}{3} = \underline{\ ?\ }$

4. Which is another way to think about this problem?

   $\frac{3}{4} \times 16 = 12$

   A. $\frac{4}{3} \times 16 = 12$ B. $\frac{3}{4} \times 16 = 12$

   C. $4 \times \frac{16}{3} = 12$ D. $3 \times \frac{16}{4} = 12$

T R Y   I T

Fraction Multiplication (B)

Multiply Fractions

1. Use an area grid model to solve each problem and explain your thinking. Simplify the factors and the product, if necessary.

    (a) $\frac{2}{6} \times \frac{1}{4} = \underline{}$

    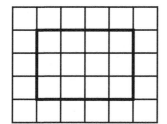

    (b) $\frac{3}{4} \times \frac{4}{5} = \underline{}$

    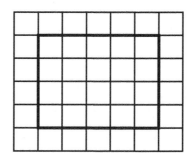

2. Write the multiplication problem and product that each diagram represents. Explain your thinking.

    (a)

    (b)
    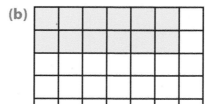

3. Write the simplified product for each problem and explain how you solved the problem.

    (a) $\frac{5}{9} \times \frac{6}{6} = \underline{}$

    (b) $\frac{8}{8} \times \frac{13}{15} = \underline{}$

TRY IT

Fraction Multiplication (C)

Fraction Multiplication

1. Use a grid model to solve each problem. Explain your thinking. Simplify the product and change to a mixed number, if necessary.

   (a) $\frac{2}{3} \times 1\frac{3}{5} = \underline{\ ?\ }$

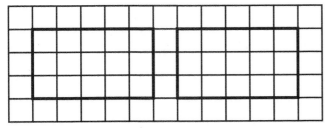

   (b) $\frac{3}{4} \times 2\frac{5}{6} = \underline{\ ?\ }$

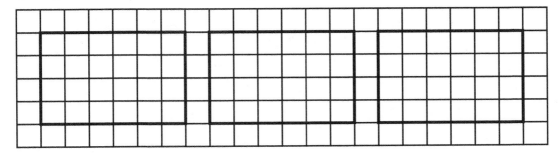

T R Y   I T

2. Use fraction circles to solve each story problem. Explain your thinking. Simplify the product and change to a mixed number, if necessary.

   (a) Antonia uses $1\frac{3}{4}$ feet of yarn to make each friendship bracelet. How many feet of yarn will Antonia use to make 3 bracelets?

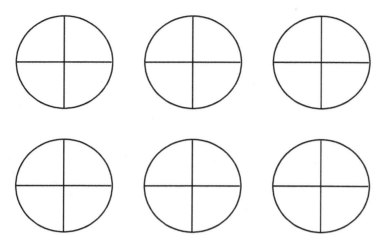

   (b) Josh is using $3\frac{2}{3}$ small boxes of raisins in his oatmeal cookies. Each box holds $\frac{3}{4}$ ounce of raisins. How many ounces of raisins will Josh use? (HINT: Use the first set of circles to multiply 3 times $\frac{3}{4}$ and use the single circle to multiply $\frac{2}{3}$ times $\frac{3}{4}$.)

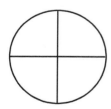

3. Use the rectangular area model to solve the problem. Explain your thinking. Simplify the product and change to a mixed number, if necessary.

   $2\frac{2}{3} \times 3\frac{1}{4} = \underline{\ ?\ }$

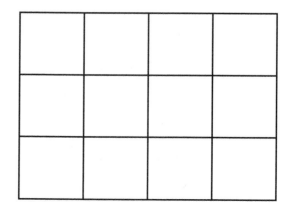

TRY IT

Fraction Multiplication (D)

More Fraction Multiplication

Memory Jogger

MULTIPLYING MIXED NUMBERS

1. Change the mixed number to an improper fraction. Rewrite the problem using the improper fraction.

2. Divide out common factors.

3. Multiply the numerators. Multiply the denominators.

4. Change the improper fraction to a mixed number.

5. Check to see if the answer can be simplified. If it can, simplify it.

Explain each step and solve the problem. Make sure your final answer is in simplest form and improper fractions are expressed as mixed numbers.

1. $\frac{4}{5} \cdot 10 = \underline{\ ?\ }$

2. $4\frac{2}{5} \cdot 3\frac{4}{7} = \underline{\ ?\ }$

Multiply. Express your answer in simplest form and rewrite improper fractions as mixed numbers.

3. $\frac{6}{10} \cdot 30 = \underline{\ ?\ }$

4. $4\frac{1}{2} \cdot 1\frac{2}{3} = \underline{\ ?\ }$

5. $\frac{5}{8} \cdot \frac{3}{10} = \underline{\ ?\ }$

6. $2\frac{1}{10} \cdot \frac{4}{7} = \underline{\ ?\ }$

TRY IT

Explain each step and solve the story problem. Make sure your final answer is in simplest form and improper fractions are expressed as mixed numbers.

7. Jordan bought 12 apples. Three-fourths of them were red. How many red apples did Jordan buy?

8. Samantha was able to shovel $3\frac{3}{4}$ sidewalks in front of neighbors' houses in an hour. How many sidewalks could she shovel in $1\frac{1}{3}$ hours?

Choose the answer. Make sure the answer is in simplest form and rewrite improper fractions as mixed numbers.

9. $\frac{3}{4} \cdot 5 = ?$

    A. $\frac{3}{20}$ B. $\frac{15}{20}$

    C. $3\frac{3}{4}$ D. $5\frac{3}{4}$

10. $3\frac{1}{4} \cdot 2\frac{2}{5} = ?$

    A. $\frac{25}{20}$ B. $\frac{65}{48}$

    C. $6\frac{1}{10}$ D. $7\frac{4}{5}$

TRY IT

Multiplication as Scaling

Solve Scaling Problems

Write a scaling statement based on the equation.

For example: $3 = \frac{1}{2} \times 6 \rightarrow$ Three has half the value of six.

1. $36 = 4 \times 9$

2. $50 = 10 \times 5$

3. $\frac{2}{3} = 2 \times \frac{1}{3}$

4. $\frac{3}{4} = \frac{1}{4} \times 3$

5. $\frac{2}{5} \times 2 = \frac{4}{5}$

Choose the answer.

6. Which is greater?

   A. 6×3

   B. $6 \times \frac{3}{4}$

7. Which is greater?

   A. $\frac{121}{10}$

   B. $\frac{121}{10} \times 7$

8. Which is less?

   A. $\frac{12}{33} \times \frac{5}{2}$

   B. $\frac{12}{33} \times \frac{13}{15}$

9. Which is less?

   A. $\frac{1}{4} \times \frac{1}{3}$

   B. $4 \times \frac{1}{3}$

T R Y   I T

Answer the question and explain your reasoning.

10. Will, Candace, and Adrian built sand castles at the beach. Will noticed that Candace's sand castle was $1\frac{1}{4}$ as tall as his. He saw that Adrian's sand castle was $\frac{3}{4}$ tall as his. Who built each sand castle shown?

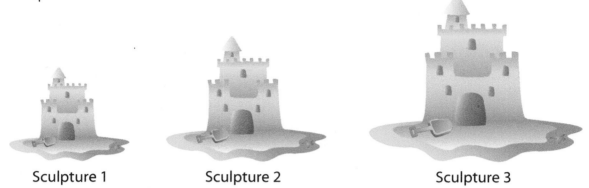

Sculpture 1   Sculpture 2   Sculpture 3

Draw a picture and explain your answer.

11. Justin, Sam, and Andra have weekend jobs mowing lawns for money. At the end of the day on Saturday, Justin had mowed $2\frac{1}{4}$ times as many lawns as Sam had and Andra had mowed $\frac{1}{2}$ as many lawns as Justin had. Who mowed the most lawns? Who mowed the least number of lawns?

TRY IT

Fractions as Division Problems

Division Problems with Fractions

Solve. Make sure each of your answers is in simplest form and that improper fractions are expressed as mixed numbers.

1. A plumber needs to cut a 6-foot long pipe into 10 equal pieces. How long will each piece be?

2. Tony and Lisa equally share babysitting for a neighbor's child. If they babysit for 7 days in 1 week, how many days will each person babysit?

3. Karen bought 15 lemons to use equally in 3 recipes of lemonade. How many lemons will go in each recipe?

4. In New York City, there are 20 blocks in a mile. Tom walks 5 blocks from the train to his office every day. What part of a mile does he walk every day?

5. Emily bought 5 pounds of ground beef and divided it into 6 equal packages to freeze. How many pounds are in each package that Emily prepares?

6. Una cut 10 feet of ribbon into 4 equal pieces. How long was each piece of ribbon?

7. Jack has 9 pounds of nails to divide equally into 12 tool belts. How many pounds will be in each belt?

Choose the answer.

8. Which means the same as $\frac{3}{7}$?

   A. $\frac{1}{3} + \frac{1}{3} + \frac{1}{3} + \frac{1}{3} + \frac{1}{3} + \frac{1}{3} + \frac{1}{3}$

   B. $\frac{3}{3} + \frac{3}{3} + \frac{3}{3}$

   C. $\frac{1}{7} + \frac{1}{7} + \frac{1}{7}$

   D. $\frac{7}{7} + \frac{7}{7} + \frac{7}{7}$

9. Which means the same as $\frac{5}{4}$?

   A. $\frac{1}{5} + \frac{1}{5} + \frac{1}{5} + \frac{1}{5}$

   B. $\frac{5}{5} + \frac{5}{5} + \frac{5}{5} + \frac{5}{5}$

   C. $\frac{1}{4} + \frac{1}{4} + \frac{1}{4} + \frac{1}{4} + \frac{1}{4}$

   D. $\frac{4}{4} + \frac{4}{4} + \frac{4}{4} + \frac{4}{4} + \frac{4}{4}$

TRY IT

Choose the answer.

10. Which means the same as $2\frac{1}{4}$?

    A. $\frac{1}{4} + \frac{1}{4} + \frac{1}{4} + \frac{1}{4} + \frac{1}{4} + \frac{1}{4} + \frac{1}{4} + \frac{1}{4} + \frac{1}{4}$

    B. $\frac{1}{4} + \frac{1}{4} + \frac{1}{4}$

    C. $\frac{1}{4} + \frac{1}{4}$

    D. $\frac{2}{2} + \frac{2}{2} + \frac{2}{2} + \frac{2}{2}$

11. There are 24 balls in a bag to be equally shared by 8 ballplayers. How many balls will each player get?

    A. 2   B. 3   C. 4   D. 8

12. Emil cut a 1-meter log into 3 equal pieces. Which number line shows the length in meters of each piece?

    A.

    B.

    C.

    D.

13. Joan's cows produced 17 gallons of milk. She fills 8 equal-sized containers with the milk. Choose the location on a number line that shows the number of gallons in each container.

    A. between 0 and 1

    B. between 1 and 2

    C. exactly 2

    D. between 2 and 3

TRY IT

Core Focus
Multiplication Stories

Stories with Fraction Multiplication

Solve.

1. Three-fourths of the 24 apples that Carol bought were for baking pies. The rest were for snacks.

    (a) How many of the apples that Carol bought were for baking pies? Explain your thinking.

    (b) How many apples were for snacks? Explain your thinking.

    (c) Carol found that $\frac{1}{3}$ of the apples she bought for baking pies had too many brown spots, so she fed those to her pigs. How many apples did Carol's pigs get? Explain your thinking.

2. Katarina practices the piano $1\frac{3}{4}$ hours per day.

    (a) Write a multiplication equation to show how many hours she practiced on Monday, Tuesday, and Wednesday combined.

    (b) Solve your equation in Part (a) and make sure your answer is in simplest mixed-number form. Show all of your work and write your answer as a complete sentence.

    (c) On both Thursday and Friday, Katarina practiced twice as long as she did on Wednesday. Write a multiplication equation to show how many hours she practiced on Thursday only.

    (d) Solve your equation in Part (c) and make sure your answer is in simplest mixed-number form. Show all of your work and write your answer as a complete sentence.

    (e) Multiply to determine how long Katarina practiced on Thursday and Friday combined. Make sure your answer is in simplest mixed-number form. Show all of your work and write your answer as a complete sentence.

3. Use this equation for all parts of this problem.
    $$\frac{7}{8} \cdot \frac{4}{5} = \underline{\quad?\quad}$$

    (a) Write a story and a question that can be answered by solving the equation.

    (b) Solve the problem you wrote and make sure your answer is in simplest form. Show all of your work and write your answer as a complete sentence.

T R Y   I T

Solve.

4. Use this equation for all parts of this problem.

$$\frac{5}{6} \cdot 9 = \underline{\ ?\ }$$

(a) Write a story and a question that can be answered by solving the equation.

(b) Solve the problem you wrote and make sure your answer is in simplest form. Show all of your work and write your answer as a complete sentence.

Think Like a Mathematician Self-Check

5. State the actions and thinking you used during this lesson as a math learner.

Math Thinking and Actions
I made sense of problems by • Explaining to myself what a problem means and what it asks for • Using drawings or diagrams to represent a problem I was solving
I explained my math thinking clearly.
I tried out new ways to check if an answer is reasonable.
Other

TRY IT

Fraction Multiplication Story Problems (A)
Understand Multiplication Story Problems

Worked Examples

You can write a number sentence to set up the solution for the following multiplication story problem:

- A cabinet that you are building will be $4\frac{1}{2}$ feet tall. The doorknob needs to be placed $\frac{5}{6}$ of the way up from the bottom of the cabinet. How high should you place the doorknob?

PROBLEM 1 Write a number sentence that you can use to solve the multiplication story problem.

SOLUTION

1 Read the problem.

2 Decide what question needs to be answered. For this problem, you need to find where you will place the doorknob.

3 Decide what operation you need to use. For this problem, you need to use multiplication to find out what $\frac{5}{6}$ of $4\frac{1}{2}$ equals.

4 Write a number sentence that finds the product of the factors $4\frac{1}{2}$ and $\frac{5}{6}$.

ANSWER $4\frac{1}{2} \times \frac{5}{6} = ?$

PROBLEM 2 Solve the number sentence you wrote for Problem 1.

SOLUTION

1 Write the number sentence that solves the problem: $4\frac{1}{2} \times \frac{5}{6} = ?$

2 Change $4\frac{1}{2}$ to an improper fraction: $\frac{9}{2} \times \frac{5}{6} = ?$

3 Divide out the common factors; 3 is a common factor of 9 and 6: $\frac{3}{2} \times \frac{5}{2} = ?$

4 Multiply the numerators, and multiply the denominators: $\frac{15}{4}$

5 Change the improper fraction to a mixed number: $\frac{15}{4} = 3\frac{3}{4}$

6 $4\frac{1}{2} \times \frac{5}{6} = 3\frac{3}{4}$

ANSWER The knob should be $3\frac{3}{4}$ feet from the bottom of the cabinet.

LEARN

Write a number sentence for each problem. Then go back and solve the problems.

1. You are painting a large toy box.

   The paintbrush is $\frac{3}{10}$ feet wide.

   If it takes 9 brushstrokes to paint across the side, how long is the side?

2. You are building a kitchen table. You want to put glass inserts, or pieces, in the middle.

   If the table will be $2\frac{1}{4}$ yards in length and the length of the inserts will be $\frac{4}{6}$ of the table's length, how long will the inserts be?

3. You are repairing a closet door.

   The length of the door is $2\frac{6}{9}$ feet.

   A design on the door is $\frac{3}{4}$ of the door's length.

   What is the length of the design on the door?

4. A tree house you are building requires pieces of wood that are $2\frac{6}{12}$ feet wide.

   If $52\frac{1}{2}$ of those pieces of wood are laid side to side between tree limbs to create the floor, how wide is the floor?

5. A railing is around the tree house.

   A total of $5\frac{1}{4}$ pieces of wood that are $3\frac{2}{7}$ feet long are used to create the railing.

   How long is the railing?

LEARN

Memory Jogger

Follow these steps to solve multiplication story problems with fractions, whole numbers, and mixed numbers:

1. Read the problem.
2. Decide what question needs to be answered.
3. Decide what operation needs to be used.
4. Write the number sentence that solves the problem.
5. Change mixed numbers to improper fractions.
6. Change whole numbers to fractions with a denominator of 1.
7. Rewrite the problem, if needed.
8. Divide out the common factors, and rewrite the problem.
9. Multiply the numerators. Multiply the denominators. Write the product.
10. Simplify the product, if needed.
11. Use the product to answer the question in the problem.

Write a number sentence for the problem. Then solve the problem. Express your answer in simplest form.

1. A ball was dropped from a height of 18 meters.
   It bounced back $\frac{5}{6}$ of that original height on the first bounce.
   How high did the ball bounce back on the first bounce?

2. Mr. Jones bought $5\frac{1}{4}$ yards of fabric.
   He gave his son $\frac{3}{7}$ of the fabric.
   How much fabric did he give his son?

TRY IT

Write a number sentence for the problem. Then solve the problem.
Express your answer in simplest form.

3. Dan is painting a mural that measures $3\frac{1}{2}$ feet by $5\frac{2}{3}$ feet.

   What is the area of the mural?

4. Fred finished his book in $2\frac{1}{3}$ hours.

   Alex took $1\frac{1}{2}$ times longer than Fred to finish.

   How long did it take Alex to finish his book?

Choose the answer. Be sure the answer is in simplest form.

5. The width of a television screen is $\frac{4}{5}$
   the length. The length of the television
   screen is $3\frac{3}{4}$ feet. What is the width?

   A. 2 ft

   B. $2\frac{2}{5}$ ft

   C. $2\frac{3}{5}$ ft

   D. 3 ft

6. A recipe asks for $3\frac{1}{2}$ cups of milk.
   How much milk is needed to make
   $1\frac{1}{2}$ recipes?

   A. $4\frac{1}{4}$ cups

   B. $4\frac{1}{2}$ cups

   C. $5\frac{1}{4}$ cups

   D. $5\frac{1}{2}$ cups

TRY IT

Fraction Multiplication Story Problems (B)

Understand Fraction Story Problems

Worked Examples

You can write an equation to set up the solution for the following story problem:

- Avery and his father are making pizzas for a party. They want to put $1\frac{1}{6}$ cups of sauce on each of their 8 pizzas. How many cups of sauce will Avery and his father need?

PROBLEM 1 Write an equation that you can use to solve the story problem.

SOLUTION

1. Read the problem.

2. Decide what question needs to be answered. For this problem, you need to find how many cups of sauce Avery and his father need for the 8 pizzas.

3. Decide what operation you need to use. For this problem, you need to multiply to find the product of $1\frac{1}{6}$ and 8.

4. Write an equation that would solve this problem.

ANSWER $1\frac{1}{6} \times 8 = ?$

PROBLEM 2 Solve the equation you wrote for Problem 1.

SOLUTION

1. Write the equation that solves the problem: $1\frac{1}{6} \times 8 = ?$

2. Change $1\frac{1}{6}$ and 8 to improper fractions: $\frac{7}{6} \times \frac{8}{1} = ?$

3. Divide out the common factors; 2 is a common factor of 6 and 8.
$\frac{7}{3} \times \frac{4}{1} = ?$

4. Multiply the numerators, and multiply the denominators: $\frac{28}{3}$

5. Change the improper fraction to a mixed number: $\frac{28}{3} = 9\frac{1}{3}$

6. $1\frac{1}{6} \times 8 = 9\frac{1}{3}$

ANSWER Avery and his father need $9\frac{1}{3}$ cups of sauce for 8 pizzas.

LEARN

You can write an equation to set up the solution for the following story problem:

- For dessert, Avery and his father are baking brownies. The recipe calls for $2\frac{5}{6}$ cups of flour. They want to make $1\frac{1}{2}$ times the recipe. How much flour should Avery and his father use?

PROBLEM 3 Write an equation that you can use to solve the story problem.

SOLUTION

1 Read the problem.

2 Decide what question needs to be answered. For this problem, you need to find how much flour Avery and his father should use to make $1\frac{1}{2}$ times the brownie recipe.

3 Decide what operation you need to use. For this problem, you need to use multiplication to find out what $2\frac{5}{6}$ times $1\frac{1}{2}$ equals.

4 Write an equation that finds the product of the factors $2\frac{5}{6}$ and $1\frac{1}{2}$.

ANSWER $2\frac{5}{6} \times 1\frac{1}{2} = ?$

PROBLEM 4 Solve the equation you wrote for Problem 3.

SOLUTION

1 Write the equation that solves the problem: $2\frac{5}{6} \times 1\frac{1}{2} = ?$

2 Change $2\frac{5}{6}$ and $1\frac{1}{2}$ to improper fractions: $\frac{17}{6} \times \frac{3}{2} = ?$

3 Divide out the common factors; 3 is a common factor of 6 and 3: $\frac{17}{2} \times \frac{1}{2} = ?$

4 Multiply the numerators, and multiply the denominators: $\frac{17}{4}$

5 Change the improper fraction to a mixed number: $\frac{17}{4} = 4\frac{1}{4}$

6 $2\frac{5}{6} \times 1\frac{1}{2} = 4\frac{1}{4}$

ANSWER Avery and his father should use $4\frac{1}{4}$ cups of flour.

Write an equation for each problem. Then go back and solve the problems.

1. The chef made 10 trays of lasagna this morning, and $\frac{1}{8}$ of the lasagna is left. How many trays of lasagna are left?

2. On the lunch menu, $\frac{4}{12}$ of the meals are sandwiches. Mayonnaise is on $\frac{7}{8}$ of the sandwiches. What fraction of meals on the menu have mayonnaise?

3. During lunch, $\frac{3}{10}$ of the customers order cheeseburgers and french fries. If there are 70 customers in the restaurant, how many customers order cheeseburgers and french fries?

4. A server can set $9\frac{4}{5}$ tables in 1 hour. How many tables can the server set in $2\frac{1}{2}$ hours?

5. This recipe is for lemonade. Avery wants to triple the recipe for a party. Calculate how much of each ingredient is needed to triple the recipe.

$1\frac{1}{4}$ cups white sugar

8 cups water

$1\frac{1}{2}$ cups lemon juice

$2\frac{1}{2}$ cups crushed ice

LEARN

Fraction Multiplication Story Problems (B)

Multiplication Story Problems with Fractions

Memory Jogger

Follow these steps to solve multiplication story problems with fractions, whole numbers, and mixed numbers:

1. Read the problem.
2. Decide what question needs to be answered.
3. Decide what operation needs to be used.
4. Write the equation that solves the problem.
5. Change mixed numbers to improper fractions.
6. Change whole numbers to fractions with a denominator of 1.
7. Rewrite the problem, if needed.
8. Divide out the common factors, and rewrite the problem.
9. Multiply the numerators. Multiply the denominators. Write the product.
10. Simplify the product, if needed.
11. Use the product to answer the question in the problem.

Write an equation for the problem. Then solve the problem. Express your answer in simplest form.

1. Marie is $4\frac{1}{2}$ years old. Riva is $1\frac{1}{3}$ times older than Marie. How old is Riva?

2. Nancy's trip is scheduled to take $1\frac{1}{5}$ hours. She has covered $\frac{2}{3}$ of the distance of her trip. How long has she been traveling so far?

Choose the answer. Be sure the answer is in simplest form.

3. The diameter on the wheels of a monster truck are $4\frac{1}{2}$ feet. Jeff is building a model $\frac{1}{3}$ the size of the monster truck. What diameter should he use for the wheels on his model?

   A. $1\frac{1}{3}$ ft   B. $1\frac{1}{2}$ ft   C. $2\frac{2}{3}$ ft   D. $13\frac{1}{2}$ ft

4. An elephant at the zoo eats $3\frac{1}{2}$ tons of food in a year. If there are 5 elephants in the zoo, how much food will they eat in a year?

   A. $15\frac{1}{2}$ tons   B. $15\frac{2}{3}$ tons   C. $17\frac{1}{2}$ tons   D. $17\frac{2}{3}$ tons

5. Debi can read $6\frac{3}{4}$ books in 1 week. How many books can she read in $3\frac{1}{3}$ weeks?

   A. 18   B. $18\frac{1}{4}$ C. $22\frac{1}{2}$ D. 24

TRY IT

Solve. Answer in simplest form.

1. Sergio is roping off his backyard rectangular garden. His garden measures $8\frac{3}{4}$ meters by $5\frac{7}{8}$ meters.

   (a) Draw and label the dimensions of a rectangle that represents the garden.

   (b) Write an equation to represent the amount of rope Sergio needs to go completely around his garden and have an additional $\frac{1}{2}$ meter for looping and tying the rope. Explain your reasoning for writing your equation as you have.

   (c) Determine the total amount of rope Sergio needs. Show your work and write your answer as a complete sentence.

   (d) Sergio finds a piece of rope in his garage that is 35 meters long. If he cuts the rope for his garden from this piece of rope, how much rope will he have left? Show your work and write your answer as a complete sentence.

   (e) Estimate to determine whether Sergio has enough rope left to cut two pieces that are $1\frac{1}{3}$ meters long and $2\frac{7}{8}$ meters long. Explain your reasoning.

TRY IT

2. State the actions and thinking you used during this lesson as a math learner.

Math Thinking and Actions
I made sense of problems by   • Explaining to myself what a problem means and what it asks for   • Using drawings or diagrams to represent a problem I was solving
I explained my math thinking clearly.
I tried out new ways to check if an answer is reasonable.
Other

TRY IT

Compare Decimals

Greater or Less?

You can use a greater-than symbol (>) to order and compare numbers from greatest to least. You can use a less-than symbol (<) to order and compare numbers from least to greatest.

PROBLEM Use > and < to write two statements to compare 320.3 and 320.03.

SOLUTION

1 Write numbers with the same number of decimal places, if needed.

320.30 and 320.03

2 Start at the far left place-value position. Find the first pair of digits that differ. Compare them.

3 tenths > 0 tenths

3 Write a comparison statement using the numbers 320.3 and 320.03 from the original problem.

320.3 > 320.03

4 Reverse the order of the numbers 320.3 and 320.03 from the original problem and use the correct symbol to compare them.

320.03 < 320.3

ANSWER 320.3 > 320.03; 320.03 < 320.3

Use > and < to write **two** statements to compare the numbers.

1. 1,323.99 and 1,324.01

2. 203.02 and 20.32

3. 78.45 and 78.48

Use <, >, or = to compare the numbers.

4. 106.06 __?__ 106.60

5. 34.3 __?__ 34.30

6. 3,482.3 __?__ 3,482.08

Solve.

7. Monya has two large dogs. Sandy weighs 50.2 pounds and Mocca weighs 50.19 pounds. Which dog weighs less, or do they weigh the same amount?

8. Caryn kicked a ball 34.62 meters. George kicked a ball 34.7 meters. Who kicked the ball farther, or did they kick the ball the same distance?

9. Molly swam 32.9 laps. Tom swam 32.90 laps. Who swam farther, or did they swim the same distance?

LEARN

Compare and Expand Decimals

Read, Write, and Expand Decimals

Worked Examples

You can read and write decimals much like you read and write whole numbers, including using expanded form.

PROBLEM 1 Read the number aloud and write it out in words: 1,235.456

SOLUTION

1 Put the decimal number into a place-value chart.

Thousands									
hundred thousands	ten thousands	thousands	hundreds	tens	ones	tenths	hundredths	thousandths
		1	**2**	**3**	**5**	**4**	**5**	**6**

2 Read the number aloud, using the digits and place-value names.

- For the whole number portion, read left to right.
- Instead of saying "decimal" or "point," say "and" for the decimal point. Saying "and" separates the whole number portion from the decimal portion of the number. This is the only time you say "and" when reading or writing a number in words.
- For the decimal portion, read the number as if it were a whole number but end with the final place value on the right.

3 Write the number in words.

ANSWER One thousand two hundred thirty-five and four hundred fifty-six thousandths.

LEARN

PROBLEM 2 Write the numerals for the following number:

twenty-five thousand four hundred seven and thirteen hundredths

Use the place-value chart, if necessary.

1 Find the "and" in the description. Write the numerals for all the words given before the "and" using the digits and the place values.

25,407

2 After writing the whole-number portion, write the decimal point and then the digits and place values for all the words after the "and."

ANSWER 25,407.13

PROBLEM 3 Write the expanded form: 348.29

1 Use a place-value chart to help, placing the digits in their appropriate columns.

Thousands				hundreds	tens	ones		tenths	hundredths	thousandths
hundred thousands	ten thousands	thousands	,	3	4	8	·	2	9	

2 Under the chart, label each column with its appropriate number value. The hundreds place is 100, the tens place is 10, the ones place is 1, the tenths place is $\frac{1}{10}$, and the hundredths place is $\frac{1}{100}$.

3 Write the expanded form. When writing the expanded form of a number, each digit is written, then multiplied by the place value, and the products are added together.

ANSWER $3 \times 100 + 4 \times 10 + 8 \times 1 + 2 \times \frac{1}{10} + 9 \times \frac{1}{100}$

LEARN

PROBLEM 4 Write the expanded form: 32,027.307

1 Use a place-value chart to help, placing the digits in their appropriate columns.

	Thousands									
hundred thousands	ten thousands	thousands	hundreds	tens	ones	tenths	hundredths	thousandths
	3	2	0	2	7 .	3	0	7

2 Using the place values for each digit, write out the expanded form.

ANSWER

$3 \times 10,000 + 2 \times 1,000 + 0 \times 100 + 2 \times 10 + 7 \times 1 + 3 \times \frac{1}{10} + 0 \times \frac{1}{100} + 7 \times \frac{1}{1,000}$

Read the number aloud and then write the number in words.

1. 12,250.17

2. 142,426.076

Write the numerals for the decimal number written in words.

3. two hundred five thousand, six hundred thirty-seven and seven hundredths

4. three hundred twenty-four thousand, thirty-seven and eight hundred six thousandths

Write the decimal number in expanded form.

5. 12,250.13

6. 438,957.239

Order Three Decimal Numbers

Order Numbers

Worked Examples

You can order decimal numbers in the same way that you order whole numbers. You start at the left-most digit and compare the values of the digits in the same place-value position. You find the greatest number, the least number, and the number in-between these numbers. Then you order the numbers and insert greater-than symbols (>) or less-than symbols (<) as directed.

PROBLEM A bag of raisins weighs 5.34 ounces. A bag of dried peaches weighs 5.7 ounces. A bag of dried apricots weighs 4.98 ounces. What comparison statement shows the weight of the fruit ordered from least to greatest?

SOLUTION

1 Refer to this place-value chart, if you wish.

Millions		Hundred Thousands	Ten Thousands	Thousands		Hundreds	Tens	Ones		Tenths	Hundredths	Thousandths
	,				,				.			

2 Make a chart to organize your numbers.

Greatest	
In-Between	
Least	

3 To compare 5.34, 5.7, 4.98, start at the left-most digit and compare the values of the digits in the same place-value position. First find the greatest and least numbers.

In the ones place, 4 is less than the two 5s, so 4.98 is the least number. Write it in the chart and cross it off the list.

In the tenths place, 7 is greater than 3, so 5.7 is the greatest number. Write it in the chart and cross it off the list. (Write 5.7 as 5.70, if you wish.)

L E A R N

Greatest	5.7
In-Between	
Least	4.98

5.34
~~5.7~~
~~4.98~~

The number that remains, 5.34, is in-between the greatest and least numbers. Write it in the chart and cross it off the list.

Greatest	5.7
In-Between	5.34
Least	4.98

~~5.34~~
~~5.7~~
~~4.98~~

4 Read the problem again and order from least to greatest: 4.98, 5.34, 5.7.

5 Use less-than symbols ($<$) to write a comparison statement: $4.98 < 5.34 < 5.7$.

ANSWER $4.98 < 5.34 < 5.7$

Read the problem and follow the directions.

1. Write 513.45, 514.5, and 154.1 in order from greatest to least.

2. Write 627.45, 672.45, and 627.5 in order from least to greatest.

3. A bag of raisins weighs 5.34 ounces. A bag of dried peaches weighs 5.7 ounces. A bag of dried apricots weighs 4.98 ounces. Order the names of the fruit from the greatest weight to the least weight.

LEARN

Solve.

4. Maya incorrectly wrote a comparison statement to order 3.4, 3.04, and 3.14 from greatest to least this way:
3.4 > 3.04 > 3.14.

Why is her answer incorrect?

5. Jeff incorrectly wrote a comparison statement to order 25.4, 23.9, and 25.29 from least to greatest this way:
25.4 > 25.29 > 23.9.

Why is his answer incorrect?

6. A bag of raisins weighs 5.34 ounces. A bag of dried peaches weighs 5.7 ounces. A bag of dried apricots weighs 4.98 ounces.

What comparison statement shows the weight of the fruit ordered from least to greatest?

Use the table to solve.

7. In a swim race, the fastest time, or least number of seconds, wins the race. Write the names of the swimmers in order from fastest to slowest times for the race.

50-Meter Race Results	
Name	Seconds
Kate	57.8
Jake	59.01
Ivy	58.8
Dean	57.35
Aiden	57.83

LEARN

Order Three Decimal Numbers

Write Comparison Statements

Complete the comparison statement.

1. 37.12, 37.2, 37.02
   $\underline{\ ?\ } < \underline{\ ?\ } < \underline{\ ?\ }$

2. 100.09, 99.10, 100.9
   $\underline{\ ?\ } > \underline{\ ?\ } > \underline{\ ?\ }$

Read the problem and follow the directions.

3. Bea rode her bike 18.49 miles. Tina rode her bike 18.04 miles. Rob rode his bike 18.45 miles. Use two > symbols to order the miles from greatest to least.

4. Bea rode her bike 18.49 miles. Tina rode her bike 18.04 miles. Rob rode his bike 18.45 miles. Use two < symbols to order the miles from least to greatest.

5. Write the decimals 45.78, 45.7, and 45.87 in order from least to greatest.

6. Write the decimals 33.06, 33.64, and 33.60 in order from greatest to least.

7. Cheryl threw the ball 15.6 meters. Gina threw the ball 15.72 meters. Joanne threw the ball 15.67 meters. Marta threw the ball 15.06 meters. Write the names of the girls in order from the longest throw to the shortest throw.

8. Susana used 6.75 cubic feet of soil. Rob used 6.07 cubic feet of soil. Lucy used 6.55 cubic feet of soil. Matt used 6.25 cubic feet of soil. Write the names of the children in order from the least soil used to the most soil used.

9. Bea rode her bike 18.49 miles. Tina rode her bike 18.04 miles. Rob rode his bike 18.45 miles. Order the names from the longest to the shortest distance they rode.

TRY IT

Choose the answer.

10. Which shows the decimals 56.7, 56.73, and 56.37 written in order from greatest to least?

   A. 56.73, 56.7, 56.37

   B. 56.7, 56.37, 56.73

   C. 56.73, 56.37, 56.7

   D. 56.7, 56.73, 56.37

11. Corrine compared the decimals 11.46, 11.98, and 11.34. Which is correct?

   A. $11.46 > 11.98 > 11.34$

   B. $11.34 > 11.46 > 11.98$

   C. $11.98 > 11.34 > 11.46$

   D. $11.98 > 11.46 > 11.34$

12. Peter compared the decimals 794.77, 794.99, and 794.33. Which is correct?

   A. $794.77 < 794.99 < 794.33$

   B. $794.33 < 794.77 < 794.99$

   C. $794.99 < 794.77 < 794.33$

   D. $794.33 < 794.99 < 794.77$

13. Megan compared the decimals 66.64, 66.46, and 64.66. Which is correct?

   A. $66.64 < 64.66 < 66.46$

   B. $64.66 < 66.46 < 66.64$

   C. $66.46 < 66.64 < 64.66$

   D. $66.64 < 66.46 < 64.66$

14. Jeff weighs 77.4 pounds. Gordon weighs 77.82 pounds. Lucas weighs 77.28 pounds. Xander weighs 77.04 pounds. Which shows these boys ordered from the least weight to the greatest weight?

   A. Jeff, Gordon, Lucas, Xander

   B. Gordon, Xander, Lucas, Jeff

   C. Lucas, Jeff, Xander, Gordon

   D. Xander, Lucas, Jeff, Gordon

15. Joseph bought a packet of tortillas that weighed 1.35 pounds. Martin bought a packet of tortillas that weighed 1.55 pounds. Phil bought a packet of tortillas that weighed 1.85 pounds. Arnold bought a packet of tortillas that weighed 1.65 pounds. Write the names of the boys in order from the heaviest packet of tortillas bought to the lightest packet of tortillas bought.

   A. Phil, Arnold, Martin, Joseph

   B. Arnold, Martin, Phil, Joseph

   C. Martin, Phil, Arnold, Joseph

   D. Joseph, Martin, Phil, Arnold

Challenge Question

Solve.

16. Three food choices cost $2.89, $2.09, and $2.98. Hot dogs cost less than hamburgers. Hamburgers cost more than veggie burgers. Veggie burgers cost more than hot dogs. Use $<$ or $>$ to order the prices from greatest to least. Then write the names of the foods in order from least to most expensive.

TRY IT

Round Decimals Through Hundredths

Practice Rounding Decimals

Round the decimal number to the given place value.

1. 37.984 to the nearest hundredth

2. 311.65 to the nearest tenth

3. 43.652 to the nearest tenth

4. 123.712 to the nearest tenth

Solve by rounding to the given place value.

5. Pedro keeps a record of the amount of gasoline he buys for his lawn-mowing service. His records show that he bought 138.93 gallons of gasoline this summer. About how many gallons of gas did Pedro buy this summer, rounded to the nearest tenth of a gallon?

6. The gas pump shows that Kelly bought 16.571 gallons of gas. About how many gallons of gas did Kelly buy, rounded to the nearest hundredth of a gallon?

Choose the answer.

7. What is 375.45 rounded to the nearest tenth?

   A. 370
   B. 375.4
   C. 375.5
   D. 380

8. What is 175.472 rounded to the nearest tenth?

   A. 175
   B. 175.4
   C. 175.5
   D. 180

9. What is 32.632 rounded to the nearest hundredth?

   A. 32.6
   B. 32.63
   C. 32.7
   D. 33

10. What is 76.925 rounded to the nearest whole number?

    A. 77
    B. 76.93
    C. 76.9
    D. 76

TRY IT

Decimal Addition

Addition with Decimals

Add.

1. $33.72 + 28.8$

2. $987.23 + 85.22$

3. $122.1 + 18.98$

4. $856.32 + 76.08 + 15.3$

Add. Show all your work and fully explain your reasoning, including why you set up the problem as you did.

5. $360.72 + 89 + 0.5$

Decimal Subtraction

Subtracting with Decimals

Solve.

1. $98.4 - 23.65 = \underline{\ ?\ }$

2. $77.63 - 9.3 = \underline{\ ?\ }$

3. $639.2 - 42.12 = \underline{\ ?\ }$

4. $123.43 - 3.4 = \underline{\ ?\ }$

Subtract. Show all work and fully explain your reasoning, including why you set up the problem as you did.

5. $856 - 73.78 = ?$

Show how to use addition to check the answer to this problem. Explain why this method of checking works.

6. $15.63 - 6.7 = 8.93$

TRY IT

Solve Story Problems with Decimals

Solve Problems with Decimals

Solve.

1. Jeff bought 15.5 meters of red felt and 8.75 meters of green felt.

    How much felt did Jeff buy?

2. In 1996, the world record for distance traveled on a bicycle in 1 hour was 56.37 kilometers. In 1984, the record was 51.1 kilometers.

    How much longer is the 1996 record than the 1984 record?

3. The Willot family owns two Great Danes. The male dog weighs 150.3 pounds. The female dog weighs 135.35 pounds.

    How many more pounds does the male dog weigh than the female dog?

Choose the answer.

4. In 2008, the world record for the men's outdoor shot put was 23.12 meters. The world record for the women's outdoor shot put was 22.63 meters.

    How much longer is the men's record than the women's record?

    A. 0.49 meters

    B. 1.49 meters

    C. 1.51 meters

    D. 1.59 meters

5. On Monday, 1.12 inches of rain fell. On Tuesday, another 2.59 inches of rain fell.

    What was the total rainfall in the two days?

    A. 3.62 inches

    B. 3.71 inches

    C. 3.72 inches

    D. 3.73 inches

6. Joel spent $15.23 on a gift for his sister and $18.90 on a gift for his mother.

    How much did Joel spend altogether?

    A. $33.13

    B. $34.03

    C. $34.13

    D. $34.23

7. Freddy rode his bike 18.12 kilometers on Saturday and 13.5 kilometers on Sunday.

    How far did Freddy ride his bike in the two days?

    A. 21.62 kilometers

    B. 31.12 kilometers

    C. 31.13 kilometers

    D. 31.62 kilometers

TRY IT

Estimate Decimal Sums and Differences

Decimal Sum and Difference Estimation

Solve.

1. Round each number to the nearest hundredth and estimate the sum:
   450.303 + 120.661

2. Estimate by rounding each number to the nearest tenth and then subtract:
   122.63 − 10.48

3. Estimate by rounding each number to the nearest hundredth and then subtract:
   360.727 − 89.852

4. Solve by first rounding each number to the nearest hundredth.

   Paula is keeping a record of the rainfall in her community for a science project. The rainfall was 8.496 inches last month and 3.188 inches this month. About how much rain fell in both months combined?

Choose the answer.

5. Solve by first rounding each number to the nearest tenth.

   Jacob's first throw of the shot put was 23.12 meters and his second throw was 22.63 meters. About how much longer was Jacob's first throw than his second?

   A. 0.5 meters

   B. 0.49 meters

   C. 0.4 meters

   D. 0.3 meters

TRY IT

Solve.

1. Alexander is explaining to his younger brother the relationships among place values in this number:

   222.22

   Fill in the appropriate value for each of Alexander's statements and explain your answer.

   (a) "The 2 in the hundredths place is _____ times the value of the 2 in the tenths place."

   (b) "The 2 in the tens place is _____ times the value of the 2 in the hundreds place."

   (c) "The 2 in the ones place is _____ times the value of the 2 in the tenths place."

2. An elevator can hold up to 1,100 pounds. Three people enter the elevator. One person weighs 230.25 pounds, another weighs 136.8 pounds, and the third person weighs 185 pounds. They push a loaded cart into the elevator that weighs 353.4 pounds. Answer each question and show all work.

   (a) What is the combined weight of the three people?

   (b) How much less does the loaded cart weigh than the three people?

   (c) What is the maximum weight that another person entering the elevator could weigh and not go over the elevator's weight capacity? Explain your work.

TRY IT

3. Jocelyn bought several pounds of fruit at the grocery store. The amount she spent for each type of fruit is shown in the table.

Fruit	Cost ($)
apples	3.35
pears	4.68
grapes	1.96
oranges	5.43

(a) Round each value to the nearest dime. Show each rounded value.

(b) Jocelyn pays the cashier with two $10 bills. Use the rounded values from Part (a) to calculate how much change she will receive. Show and explain your work.

(c) Determine the exact amount of change Jocelyn will receive. What is the difference between the actual amount and the estimate? Show and explain your work.

Think Like a Mathematician Self-Check

4. State the actions and thinking you used during this lesson as a math learner.

Math Thinking and Actions
I made sense of problems by • Explaining to myself what a problem means and what it asks for • Using drawings or diagrams to represent a problem I was solving
I explained my math thinking clearly.
I tried out new ways to check if an answer is reasonable.
Other

TRY IT

Multiply and Divide by Powers of 10

Multiply and Divide Decimals by Powers of 10

Worked Examples

The place-value system is based on powers of 10:

$$10^0 = 1 \text{ (ones place)}$$
$$10^1 = 10 \text{ (tens place)}$$
$$10^2 = 100 \text{ (hundreds place)}$$
$$10^3 = 1{,}000 \text{ (thousands place)}$$
and so on...

Notice that the exponent in the power of 10 matches the number of zeros in the value of the number. For example, 100 has 2 zeros, and the exponent on 10^2 is 2.

When you multiply or divide by powers of 10, you just change the location of the decimal point. You can multiply by powers of 10 simply by moving the decimal point to the right the number of places shown by the exponent on the 10 (or the number of zeros in the power of 10, if written out). When dividing, move the decimal point to the left the number of places shown by the power of 10. Remember that the decimal point is always located after the ones place, so in the whole number 23, the decimal point is located after the 3 ones.

PROBLEM 1 Find the following products:

- 12.4×10^1
- 12.4×10^2
- 12.4×10^3

SOLUTION When you multiply by a power of 10, you increase the place value of each digit by that power as you move the decimal to the right.

Hundreds	Tens	Ones	.	Tenths
	1	2	.	4

$$\times 10^1$$

Hundreds	Tens	Ones	.	Tenths
1	2	4	.	0

L E A R N

Thousands	,	Hundreds	Tens	Ones	.	Tenths
	,		1	2	.	4

$$\times\ 10^2$$

Thousands	,	Hundreds	Tens	Ones	.	Tenths
1	,	2	4	0	.	0

Ten Thousands	Thousands	,	Hundreds	Tens	Ones	.	Tenths
		,		1	2	.	4

$$\times\ 10^3$$

Ten Thousands	Thousands	,	Hundreds	Tens	Ones	.	Tenths
1	2	,	4	0	0	.	0

You can see that each of these answers has the digits 1, 2, and 4 in the same order as the original first factor, 12.4. Multiplying by the power of 10 just moved the decimal point to the right. The decimal moved 1 place when multiplying by 10, which is 10^1; 2 places when multiplying by 10^2; and 3 places when multiplying by 10^3. Here is 12.4×10^3 with the movement of the decimal shown:

$$12.4\underline{00}$$

The decimal point moved 3 places to the right because the factor was 10^3. In this example, notice that 2 zeros were needed to create the places you needed for your product, which is called *annexing* zeros.

ANSWER

- 124
- 1,240
- 12,400

LEARN

PROBLEM 2 Find the product by moving the decimal point.

1.456×10^2

SOLUTION Move the decimal 2 places to the right, since the exponent in 10^2 is 2.

145.6

ANSWER 145.6

PROBLEM 3 Find the following quotients:

- $3{,}472 \div 10^1$
- $3{,}472 \div 10^2$
- $3{,}472 \div 10^3$

SOLUTION When you divide by a power of 10, you decrease the place value of each digit by that power as you move the decimal to the left.

Thousands	,	Hundreds	Tens	Ones	.	Tenths	Hundredths	Thousandths
3	,	4	7	2	.			

$\div 10^1$

Thousands	,	Hundreds	Tens	Ones	.	Tenths	Hundredths	Thousandths
		3	4	7	.	2		

Thousands	,	Hundreds	Tens	Ones	.	Tenths	Hundredths	Thousandths
3	,	4	7	2	.			

$\div 10^2$

Thousands	,	Hundreds	Tens	Ones	.	Tenths	Hundredths	Thousandths
			3	4	.	7	2	

L E A R N

Thousands	,	Hundreds	Tens	Ones	.	Tenths	Hundredths	Thousandths
3	,	4	7	2	.			

$$\div 10^3$$

Thousands	,	Hundreds	Tens	Ones	.	Tenths	Hundredths	Thousandths
				3	.	4	7	2

You can see that each of these answers has the digits 3, 4, 7, and 2 in the same order as the dividend of 3,472. Dividing by the power of 10 just moved the decimal point to the left. The decimal moved 1 place when dividing by 10, which is 10^1; 2 places when dividing by 10^2; and 3 places when dividing by 10^3. Here is $3,472 \div 10^3$ with the movement of the decimal shown:

3.472

The decimal point moved 3 places to the left because the divisor was 10^3.

ANSWER

- 347.2
- 34.72
- 3.472

Be sure to move the decimal to the **left when dividing** by a power of 10 and to the **right when multiplying** by a power of 10.

PROBLEM 4 Find the quotient by moving the decimal point.

$5.8 \div 10^2$

SOLUTION Move the decimal 2 places to the left, since the exponent in 10^2 is 2.

0.058

ANSWER 0.058

LEARN

Determine the product or quotient by moving the decimal.

1. 56.34×10^2

2. 3.06×10

3. $8.2 \div 10^2$

4. 99×10^4

5. 0.42×10^3

6. 0.07×10^5

7. $300.06 \div 10$

8. $86{,}743.2 \div 10^2$

LEARN

Expand and Compare Decimal Numbers

Compare Decimals by Place Value

Worked Examples

You can use a greater-than symbol (>) to order and compare numbers from greatest to least. You can use a less-than symbol (<) to order and compare numbers from least to greatest.

PROBLEM Use > and < to write two statements to compare 320.3 and 320.03.

SOLUTION

1. Write numbers with the same number of decimal places, if needed.   320.30 and 320.03

2. Start at the far left place-value position. Find the first pair of digits that differ. Compare them.   3 tenths > 0 tenths

3. Write a comparison statement using the numbers 320.3 and 320.03 from the original problem.   320.3 > 320.03

4. Reverse the order of the numbers 320.3 and 320.03 from the original problem and use the correct symbol to compare them.   320.03 < 320.3

ANSWER 320.3 > 320.03, 320.03 < 320.3

Use > and < to write **two** statements to compare the numbers.

1. 1,399.09 and 1,399.9

2. 550.55 and 55.55

3. 78.87 and 78.78

Use <, >, or = to compare the numbers.

4. 166.06 _?_ 106.60

5. 4.4 _?_ 4.40

6. 3,482.3 _?_ 3,482.08

LEARN

Solve.

7. Patrice donated two boxes of books to the library. The first box weighs 70.2 pounds and the second box weighs 70.19 pounds. Which box weighs less, or do they weigh the same amount?

8. Nancy's paper airplane flew 34.09 meters. Karl's paper airplane flew 34.10 meters. Which paper airplane flew farther, or did they fly the same distance?

9. Cyndi jumped rope for 32.9 seconds. Derek jumped rope for 32.90 seconds. Who jumped longer, or did they jump the same amount of time?

LEARN

Round to Estimate Decimal Products and Quotients

Round to Estimate Products and Quotients

Use the given strategy to estimate the product or quotient. Explain your answer.

1. 0.471×6.379
   Round factors to the nearest tenth.

2. $0.893 \div 3.102$
   Round the dividend to the nearest tenth and the divisor to the nearest whole number.

Estimate the product or quotient. Choose the answer.

3. 3.09×304.87

   A. 9.0   B. 9.9

   C. 90   D. 900

4. 78.101×4.912

   A. 0.4   B. 4.0

   C. 40   D. 400

5. $102.02 \div 4.011$

   A. 25   B. 250

   C. 2,500   D. 25,000

6. $456,021.011 \div 10.002$

   A. 45,000   B. 4,500

   C. 450   D. 45

T R Y   I T

Multiply and Divide Decimals (A)

Multiply a Whole Number by a Decimal

Worked Examples

You can use a step-by-step approach, or an algorithm, to find the product of a decimal number and a whole number.

PROBLEM 1 $0.9 \times 3 = ?$

SOLUTION Follow the steps to multiply a number in tenths by a whole number.

1 Write the problem vertically. ————————————→

$$\begin{array}{r} 0.9 \\ \times\ 3 \\ \hline \end{array}$$

2 Multiply the digits. The result is actually 27 tenths, since you ————→ have 3 groups of 9 tenths.

$$\begin{array}{r} 0.9 \\ \times\ 3 \\ \hline 27 \end{array}$$

3 Place the decimal point in your answer according to its place value. ———→ Because you multiplied tenths by ones, the answer is expressed as tenths. Check the place value by using fractions to multiply.

$$\begin{array}{r} 0.9 \\ \times\ 3 \\ \hline 2.7 \end{array}$$

4 Use fractions to make sure tenths are correct for expressing the answer.

$$\frac{9}{10} \times 3 = \frac{9}{10} \times \frac{3}{1} = \frac{27}{10} = 2\frac{7}{10}$$

ANSWER $0.9 \times 3 = 2.7$

PROBLEM 2 $2 \times 0.87 = ?$

SOLUTION Follow the steps to multiply a whole number by a number in hundredths.

1 Write the problem vertically. ————————————→

$$\begin{array}{r} 0.87 \\ \times\ \ 2 \\ \hline \end{array}$$

2 Multiply the digits. The result is actually 174 hundredths, since ————→ you have 2 groups of 87 hundredths.

$$\begin{array}{r} {\scriptstyle 1\ 1} \\ 0.87 \\ \times\ \ 2 \\ \hline 174 \end{array}$$

L E A R N

3 Place the decimal point in your answer according to its place value. Because you multiplied hundredths by ones, the answer is expressed as hundredths. Check the place value by using fractions to multiply.

$$\begin{array}{r} \overset{1\ 1}{0.87} \\ \times\ \ 2 \\ \hline 1.74 \end{array}$$

4 Use fractions to make sure hundredths are correct for expressing the answer.

$$2 \times \frac{87}{100} = \frac{2}{1} \times \frac{87}{100} = \frac{174}{100} = 1\frac{74}{100}$$

ANSWER $2 \times 0.87 = 1.74$

PROBLEM 3 $5.231 \times 3 = ?$

SOLUTION Follow the steps to multiply a number in thousandths by a whole number.

1 Write the problem vertically.

$$\begin{array}{r} 5.231 \\ \times\ \ \ \ 3 \end{array}$$

2 Multiply the digits. The result is actually 15,693 thousandths, since you have 3 groups of 5 and 231 thousandths.

$$\begin{array}{r} 5.231 \\ \times\ \ \ \ 3 \\ \hline 15693 \end{array}$$

3 Place the decimal point in your answer according to its place value. Because you multiplied thousandths by ones, the answer is expressed as thousandths.

$$\begin{array}{r} 5.231 \\ \times\ \ \ \ 3 \\ \hline 15.693 \end{array}$$

ANSWER $5.231 \times 3 = 15.693$

Estimate the product. Find the exact answer using an algorithm. Compare the exact answer to the estimated answer to see if the exact answer is reasonable.

1. $2 \times 1.2 = ?$

2. $3 \times 0.33 = ?$

Multiply and Divide Decimals (A)

Multiply a Decimal by a Decimal

Worked Examples

You can use a step-by-step approach, or an algorithm, to find the product of two decimal numbers.

PROBLEM 1 $0.8 \times 0.4 = ?$

SOLUTION Follow the steps to multiply two numbers in tenths.

1 Write the problem vertically.
$$\begin{array}{r} 0.8 \\ \times\, 0.4 \\ \hline \end{array}$$

2 Multiply the digits. The result is actually 32 hundredths, since you have tenths multiplied by tenths. $\left(\frac{1}{10} \times \frac{1}{10} = \frac{1}{100}\right)$
$$\begin{array}{r} 0.8 \\ \times\, 0.4 \\ \hline 32 \end{array}$$

3 Place the decimal point in your answer according to its place value. Because tenths multiplied by tenths is hundredths, the number of decimal places to the right of the decimal would be two places. Check the place value by using fractions to multiply.
$$\begin{array}{r} 0.8 \\ \times\, 0.4 \\ \hline 0.32 \end{array}$$

4 Use fractions to make sure hundredths are correct for expressing the answer. $\quad\frac{8}{10} \times \frac{4}{10} = \frac{32}{100}$

ANSWER $0.8 \times 0.4 = 0.32$

PROBLEM 2 $4.08 \times 0.25 = ?$

SOLUTION Follow the steps to multiply two numbers in hundredths.

1 Write the problem vertically.
$$\begin{array}{r} 4.08 \\ \times\, 0.25 \\ \hline \end{array}$$

2 Multiply the digits. The result is actually 10,200 ten thousandths, since you have hundredths multiplied by hundredths. $\left(\frac{1}{100} \times \frac{1}{100} = \frac{1}{10,000}\right)$
$$\begin{array}{r} {}^{1}\!\!\!4.08 \\ \times\, 0.25 \\ \hline 2040 \\ +\, 8160 \\ \hline 10200 \end{array}$$

3 Place the decimal point in your answer according to its place value. Because hundredths multiplied by hundredths is ten thousandths, the number of decimal places to the right of the decimal would be four places. Check the place value by using fractions to multiply.

$$\begin{array}{r} \overset{1}{\cancel{4}}.08 \\ \times\ 0.25 \\ \hline 2040 \\ +\ 8160 \\ \hline 1.0200 \end{array}$$

This answer is the same as 1.02.

4 Use fractions to make sure ten thousandths, simplified to hundredths, are correct for expressing the answer.

$$4\frac{8}{100} \times \frac{25}{100} = \frac{408}{100} \times \frac{25}{100} = \frac{10{,}200}{10{,}000} = 1\frac{200}{10{,}000} = 1\frac{2}{100}$$

ANSWER $4.08 \times 0.25 = 1.02$

Estimate the product. Find the exact answer by using an algorithm. Compare the exact answer to the estimated answer to see if the exact answer is reasonable.

1. $0.9 \times 4.04 = ?$

2. $5.05 \times 2.22 = ?$

3. $3.25 \times 0.52 = ?$

LEARN

Multiply and Divide Decimals (A)

Practice Multiplying Decimals

Multiply. Give the exact answer.

1. $7.7 \times 0.3 = \underline{}$

2. $0.93 \times 1.8 = \underline{}$

3. $2.22 \times 4.05 = \underline{}$

4. $0.02 \times 10{,}003.9 = \underline{}$

5. $100.8 \times 300.6 = \underline{}$

6. $887.9 \times 3.9 = \underline{}$

7. $3.82 \times 14.6 = \underline{}$

Estimate the product by rounding the factors to the nearest whole number. Then find the exact answer.

8. $5.4 \times 7 = ?$

Choose the answer.

9. $0.34 \times 44.2 = ?$

   A. 15.028   B. 150.28

   C. 1,502.8   D. 15,028

10. $1.9 \times 1{,}982.34 = ?$

   A. 3,766,446   B. 376,644.6

   C. 37,664.46   D. 3,766.446

Challenge Question

Multiply. Give the exact answer.

11. $7.05 \times 3.06 = \underline{}$

T R Y I T

Multiply and Divide Decimals (B)

Divide Whole Numbers and Decimals

Worked Examples

You can use a step-by-step approach, or algorithm, to divide a decimal number by a whole number and to divide a whole number by a decimal number.

PROBLEM 1 $1.8 \div 2 = ?$

SOLUTION Follow the steps to divide a number in tenths by a whole number.

1 Use the long-division symbol to write the problem. $\longrightarrow$ $2\overline{)1.8}$
Dividing 1.8 by 2 is similar to dividing a whole number by 2.

2 Line up all place values in the dividend and quotient. The 9 in $\longrightarrow$ $2\overline{)1.8}^{\,0.9}$
the quotient should be placed above the 8. You can see that
1.8 divided by 2 is 0.9.

3 Use fractions to make sure tenths are correct for expressing the answer.

$$1\frac{8}{10} \div 2 = \frac{18}{10} \div \frac{2}{1} = \frac{\overset{9}{\cancel{18}}}{10} \times \frac{1}{\underset{1}{\cancel{2}}} = \frac{9}{10}$$

ANSWER $1.8 \div 2 = 0.9$

PROBLEM 2 $0.21 \div 7 = ?$

SOLUTION Follow the steps to divide a number in hundredths by a whole number.

1 Use the long-division symbol to write the problem. $\longrightarrow$ $7\overline{)0.21}$
Dividing 0.21 by 7 is similar to dividing a whole number by 7.
Lining up place values is important here, too.

2 Line up all place values in the dividend and quotient. The 3 $\longrightarrow$ $7\overline{)0.21}^{\,0.03}$
in the quotient needs to be above the 1, so if you place a 0
between the decimal point and the 3, you create the two places
that are needed.

3 Use fractions to make sure hundredths are correct for expressing the answer.

$$\frac{21}{100} \div 7 = \frac{21}{100} \div \frac{7}{1} = \frac{\overset{3}{\cancel{21}}}{100} \times \frac{1}{\underset{1}{\cancel{7}}} = \frac{3}{100}$$

ANSWER $0.21 \div 7 = 0.03$

L E A R N

PROBLEM 3 $6 \div 1.2 = ?$

SOLUTION Follow the steps to divide a whole number by a number in tenths.

1 Use the long-division symbol to write the problem. Dividing by a decimal number is easier if you multiply to change the divisor into a whole number. Multiply the dividend by the same number. Look at the problem as a fraction, even though it looks a little strange: $\frac{6.0}{1.2}$. Create an equivalent fraction so that 1.2 becomes a whole number. Multiply 1.2 by 10 to get 12. Both the numerator and denominator must be multiplied by the same value. Multiply 6.0 by 10.

$\longrightarrow 1.2\overline{)6.0}$

$$\frac{6.0}{1.2} \times \frac{10}{10} = \frac{60}{12}$$

2 Line up all place values in the dividend and quotient, so the 5 in the quotient should be placed above the 0. You can see that $60 \div 12 = 5$. Because $60 \div 12$ is equivalent to $6.0 \div 1.2$, the quotient of $6.0 \div 1.2$ is also 5.

$\longrightarrow \begin{array}{r} 5 \\ 12\overline{)60} \end{array}$

3 Use fractions to make sure that a whole number is correct for expressing the answer.

$$6.0 \div 1.2 = \frac{6}{1} \div 1\frac{2}{10} = 6 \div \frac{12}{10} = \frac{\overset{1}{\cancel{6}}}{1} \times \frac{10}{\underset{2}{\cancel{12}}} = \frac{10}{2} = 5$$

ANSWER $6 \div 1.2 = 5$

PROBLEM 4 $20 \div 1.25 = ?$

SOLUTION Follow the steps to divide a whole number by a number in hundredths.

1 Use the long-division symbol to write the problem. Multiply to change the divisor into a whole number. Multiply the dividend by the same number. Look at the problem as a fraction: $\frac{20}{1.25}$. Multiply the numerator and denominator by 1 in the form of $\frac{100}{100}$. Change your original fraction to an equivalent fraction that will be easier for your division problem.

$\longrightarrow 1.25\overline{)20}$

$$\frac{20}{1.25} \times \frac{100}{100} = \frac{2,000}{125}$$

2 Line up all place values in the dividend and quotient. You can see that $2,000 \div 125 = 16$. Because $2,000 \div 125$ is equivalent to $20 \div 1.25$, the quotient of $20 \div 1.25$ is also 16.

$\longrightarrow \begin{array}{r} 16 \\ 125\overline{)2,000} \\ -1,250 \\ \hline 750 \\ -750 \\ \hline 0 \end{array}$

ANSWER $20 \div 1.25 = 16$

LEARN

Estimate the quotient. Find the exact answer by using an algorithm.
Compare the exact answer to the estimated answer to see if the exact
answer is reasonable.

1. $0.25 \div 5 = ?$

2. $6 \div 1.5 = ?$

Multiply and Divide Decimals (B)

Divide a Decimal by a Decimal

Worked Examples

You can use a step-by-step approach, or algorithm, to divide a decimal number by a decimal number.

PROBLEM $13.44 \div 0.12 = ?$

SOLUTION   Follow the steps to divide a number in thousandths by a number in hundredths.

1 Look at the problem as a fraction. $\longrightarrow \dfrac{13.44}{0.12}$

2 Simplify the division by making the divisor a whole number. Multiply the divisor by 100 to change 0.12 $\longrightarrow \dfrac{13.44}{0.12} \times \dfrac{100}{100} = \dfrac{1{,}344}{12}$ to the whole number 12. Multiply the dividend by 100 to change 13.44 to 1,344.

3 Use the long-division symbol to write the new division $\longrightarrow 12\overline{)1344}$ problem.

4 Line up all place values in the dividend and quotient, so $\longrightarrow$ you can see that the quotient of $13.44 \div 12$ is 112. Because $1{,}344 \div 12$ is equivalent to $13.44 \div 0.12$, the quotient of $13.44 \div 0.12$ is also 112.

$$
\begin{array}{r}
112 \\
12\overline{)1344} \\
-12 \\
\hline
14 \\
-12 \\
\hline
24 \\
-24 \\
\hline
0
\end{array}
$$

ANSWER $13.44 \div 0.12 = 112$

Estimate the quotient. Find the exact answer by using an algorithm. Compare the exact answer to the estimated answer to see if the exact answer is reasonable.

1. $17.5 \div 3.5 = ?$ **2.** $1.12 \div 0.8 = ?$ **3.** $3.84 \div 2.4 = ?$

L E A R N

Multiply and Divide Decimals (B)

Practice Dividing Decimals

Estimate the quotient by using friendly numbers.
Then find the exact answer.

1. $14.7 \div 7 = ?$

Divide. Give the exact answer.

2. $5.84 \div 0.8 = \underline{\ ?\ }$

3. $7.2 \div 0.9 = \underline{\ ?\ }$

4. $4.48 \div 3.2 = \underline{\ ?\ }$

5. $99.88 \div 0.01 = \underline{\ ?\ }$

6. $998.91 \div 0.22 = \underline{\ ?\ }$

7. $4{,}556.29 \div 99.7 = \underline{\ ?\ }$

8. $0.17 \div 0.02 = \underline{\ ?\ }$

9. $89{,}997 \div 0.5 = \underline{\ ?\ }$

Choose the answer.

10. $8{,}997.3 \div 999.7 = ?$

    A. 9,000   B. 900   C. 90   D. 9

Challenge Question

Use the order of operations to find the answer.

11. $(1.2 \times 1.8) \div 0.6 = \underline{\ ?\ }$

TRY IT

Multiply and Divide Decimals (C)

Decimal Quotients

Worked Examples

You can use a step-by-step approach, or an algorithm, to divide a whole number by a greater whole number, resulting in a decimal quotient.

PROBLEM 1 $3 \div 10 = ?$

SOLUTION Follow the steps to divide a whole number by a greater whole number.

1. Use the long-division symbol to write the problem. ⟶ $10\overline{)3}$

2. Show the dividend as a decimal number with as many zeros as ⟶ $10\overline{)3.0}$ needed to make the division work out evenly. Add one zero after the decimal point in this dividend.

3. Line up all place values in the dividend and quotient. The 3 in the ⟶ $10\overline{)3.0}$ with 0.3 above quotient should be placed above the zero in 3.0.

4. Use fractions to make sure tenths are correct for expressing the answer. Recall that the fraction bar can also be used as a division symbol, so $3 \div 10$ is the same as $\frac{3}{10}$, 3 tenths, and 0.3.

ANSWER $3 \div 10 = 0.3$

PROBLEM 2 $6 \div 12 = ?$

SOLUTION Follow the steps to divide another whole number by a greater whole number, resulting in a decimal quotient.

1. Use the long-division symbol to write the problem. ⟶ $12\overline{)6}$

2. Show the dividend as a decimal number with as many zeros as ⟶ $12\overline{)6.0}$ needed to make the division work out evenly. Add one zero after the decimal point in this dividend.

3. Line up all place values in the dividend and quotient. The 5 in the ⟶ $12\overline{)6.0}$ with 0.5 above quotient should be placed above the zero in 6.0.

L E A R N

4 Use fractions to make sure tenths are correct for expressing the answer. Recall that the fraction bar can also be used as a division symbol, so $6 \div 12$ is the same as $\frac{6}{12}$, which simplifies to $\frac{1}{2}$ or 0.5.

ANSWER $6 \div 12 = 0.5$

PROBLEM 3 $6 \div 25 = ?$

SOLUTION Follow the steps to divide another whole number by a greater whole number, resulting in a decimal quotient.

1 Use the long-division symbol to write the problem. ⟶ $25\overline{)6}$

2 Show the dividend as a decimal number with as many zeros as ⟶ $25\overline{)6.00}$ needed to make the division work out evenly. Add two zeros after the decimal point in this dividend.

3 Line up all place values in the dividend and quotient. The 2 in the ⟶
quotient should be placed above the zero in the tenths place in 6.00, and the 4 in the quotient should be placed above the zero in the hundredths place in 6.00.

$$\begin{array}{r} 0.24 \\ 25\overline{)6.00} \\ -5.00 \\ \hline 1.00 \\ -1.00 \\ \hline 0 \end{array}$$

4 Use fractions to make sure hundredths are correct for expressing the answer. Recall that the fraction bar can also be used as a division symbol, so $6 \div 25$ is the same as $\frac{6}{25}$, which is the same as 0.24.

ANSWER $6 \div 25 = 0.24$

Use an algorithm to divide.

1. $9 \div 15 = ?$

2. $8 \div 32 = ?$

3. $7 \div 20 = ?$

Multiply and Divide Decimals (C)

Practice Multiplying and Dividing

Use $2.2 \div 1.25 = ?$ for Problems 1–4.

1. Round the dividend and the divisor to the nearest whole number. Write a number sentence to estimate the quotient. Find the estimated quotient.

2. Calculate the exact quotient.

3. Use multiplication to check the exact quotient.

4. Use the estimate to explain how you know if the exact quotient is reasonable.

Write a number sentence and estimate the product. Then find the exact product. Explain how you know if the exact answer is reasonable.

5. $6 \times 5.43 = ?$

6. $0.14 \times 0.6 = ?$

Write a number sentence and estimate the quotient. Then find the exact quotient. Explain how you know if the exact answer is reasonable.

7. $14 \div 25 = ?$

8. $7.2 \div 6 = ?$

Solve.

9. $4.5 \times 2.55 = \underline{?}$

10. $0.19 \times 201.5 = \underline{?}$

11. $0.75 \div 375 = \underline{?}$

12. $4.08 \div 0.16 = \underline{?}$

13. $117.6 \div 2.1 = \underline{?}$

Choose the answer.

14. $93.7 \times 8.1 = ?$

  A. 7.5897
  B. 75.897
  C. 758.97
  D. 7,589.7

15. $345.56 \div 5.3 = ?$

  A. 6,520
  B. 652
  C. 65.2
  D. 6.52

TRY IT

Compute Decimal Story Problems (A)

Bicycle Race Decimal Story Problems

Worked Examples

You can write a number sentence with decimal numbers and solve it to find the answer to the following story problem:

- A book about bicycle racing costs $12.95. What is the cost of 4 books?

PROBLEM 1 Write a number sentence that you can use to solve the story problem.

SOLUTION

1 Read the problem.

2 Decide what question needs to be answered. For this problem, you need to find the cost of 4 books that cost $12.95 each.

3 Decide what operation to use. For this problem, you need to use multiplication to find what $12.95 per book for 4 books equals.

4 Write a number sentence that finds the product of the factors 12.95 and 4.

ANSWER $12.95 \times 4 = ?$

PROBLEM 2 Solve the number sentence you wrote for Problem 1. Answer the question in a complete sentence.

SOLUTION

1 Write the number sentence that solves the problem. ⟶ $12.95 \times 4 = ?$

2 Write the problem vertically. Use a step-by-step process to solve the problem.
⟶
$$\begin{array}{r} 12.95 \\ \times \quad 4 \\ \hline \end{array}$$

3 Multiply. You are multiplying hundredths by a whole number, so the answer is in hundredths.
⟶
$$\begin{array}{r} {\scriptstyle 1\,3\,2} \\ 12.95 \\ \times \quad 4 \\ \hline 51.80 \end{array}$$

ANSWER The cost of 4 books on bicycle racing is $51.80.

L E A R N

Write a multiplication number sentence. Solve. Answer the question in a complete sentence.

1. The Spring Bicycle Relay has 3 stages. It takes place over 3 days. If each cyclist rides 23.76 kilometers, what is the total length of the relay?

2. One kilometer is equal to 0.62 of a mile. If a race is 134.4 kilometers, how many miles is it equivalent to?

3. Along the race route, vendors sell T-shirts for $11.55. How much will it cost to buy 8 T-shirts?

4. Vendors also have sun visors for $5.15. How much will it cost to buy 20 sun visors?

5. On average, a cyclist can bike 24 kilometers in an hour. How many kilometers will he bike in 3.6 hours?

6. The average weight of a bicycle is 17.8 pounds. What is the combined weight of 11 bicycles?

7. The Tour of the Valley is an 8-day cycling trip. If cyclists ride 45.85 kilometers a day, how many kilometers long is the trip?

8. One kilometer is equal to 0.62 miles. If a time trial is 19.6 kilometers long, how many miles is it equivalent to?

9. At the end of the Beach Front Bike Race, vendors sell T-shirts with riders' names and times on them. If each T-shirts costs $16.30, how much will 6 T-shirts cost?

10. The leader of the Beach Front Bike Race is averaging 28.3 kilometers an hour. If she rides at the same speed for the entire time, how many kilometers will she bike in 5.7 hours?

LEARN

Compute Decimal Story Problems (B)

Picnic Decimal Story Problems

You can write a number sentence with decimal numbers and solve it to find the answer to the following story problem:

- Children at a picnic sang the same song 4 times in a row. They sang for a total of 10.4 minutes. If singing the song takes the same number of minutes each time, how many minutes does it take to sing the song?

PROBLEM 1 Write a number sentence that you can use to solve the story problem.

SOLUTION

1. Read the problem.

2. Decide what question needs to be answered. For this problem, you need to find the number of minutes children would spend if they sang the song one time.

3. Decide what operation to use. For this problem, you need to use division to find the quotient of 10.4 minutes divided by 4 times.

4. Write a number sentence that finds the quotient of the dividend 10.4 and the divisor 4.

ANSWER $10.4 \div 4 = ?$

PROBLEM 2 Solve the number sentence you wrote for Problem 1. Answer the question in a complete sentence.

SOLUTION

1. Write the number sentence that solves the problem. $\longrightarrow$ $10.4 \div 4 = ?$

2. Use the long-division symbol to write the problem. $\longrightarrow$ $4\overline{)10.4}$
   Use a step-by-step process to solve the problem.

3 Divide. You are dividing tenths by a whole number, so the → answer is in tenths.

$$
\begin{array}{r}
2.6 \\
4\overline{)10.4} \\
-\,8.0 \\
\hline
2.4 \\
-\,2.4 \\
\hline
0
\end{array}
$$

ANSWER Singing the song one time takes 2.6 minutes.

Write a division number sentence. Solve. Answer the question in a complete sentece.

1. At the annual spring picnic, 15 people barbecued a total of 4.35 pounds of chicken. They each ate the same amount of chicken. How much barbecued chicken did each person eat?

2. Dana and his family drove 54.75 miles to a picnic. They traveled 36.5 miles each hour. How many hours did it take them to drive to the picnic?

3. Teresa paid $6.48 for a package of 24 paper plates. What is the price of 1 paper plate?

4. Ed made 3 pounds of tossed green salad for a picnic. When they sat down to eat, 12 people shared the salad equally. How many pounds of salad did each person have?

5. Natasha bought propane to use in the barbecue at a picnic. She paid $44.16 and bought 9.6 pounds. How much did the propane cost per pound?

6. A group of children played 5 games for a total of 2.75 hours at a picnic. Each game lasted the same amount of time. How many hours did each game last?

7. A family went on a boat ride at a picnic. The boat traveled 27.5 miles in 1.25 hours. If the boat travels at the same speed for the entire trip, how many miles did the boat travel in 1 hour?

8. The picnic tables at a park are all the same length. When 4 tables are pushed together, they form a table that measures 7.2 meters long. What is the length of 1 picnic table?

9. Rachel brought 76.5 ounces of grape juice to a picnic. She poured the juice into cups that hold 8.5 ounces each. How many cups of juice did Rachel fill?

10. Mrs. Gomez bought 3 picnic baskets for a total of $41.97. Each picnic basket cost the same price. How much did Mrs. Gomez pay for each picnic basket?

L E A R N

Compute Decimal Story Problems (C)

More Camping Trip Story Problems

Worked Examples

You can write a number sentence with decimal numbers and solve it to find the answer to the following story problem:

- Melissa drove 45.5 kilometers each hour for 6.25 hours to get to the campsite. How many kilometers did Melissa drive in all?

PROBLEM 1 Write a number sentence that you can use to solve the story problem.

SOLUTION

1 Read the problem.

2 Decide what question needs to be answered. For this problem, you need to find how many kilometers Melissa drove in 6.25 hours at a speed of 45.5 kilometers each hour.

3 Decide what operation to use. For this problem, you need to use multiplication to find the product of 6.25 and 45.5.

4 Write a number sentence that finds the product of the factors 6.25 and 45.5.

ANSWER $45.5 \times 6.25 = ?$

PROBLEM 2 Solve the number sentence you wrote for Problem 1. Answer the question in a complete sentence.

SOLUTION

1 Write the number sentence that solves the problem. $\longrightarrow 45.5 \times 6.25 = ?$

2 Write the problem vertically. Use a step-by-step process to solve the problem. $\longrightarrow$

$$
\begin{array}{r}
\overset{3\ 3}{\underset{2\ 2}{\cancel{1}\ \cancel{1}}} \\
45.5 \\
\times\ 6.25 \\
\hline
2275 \\
9100 \\
+\ 273000 \\
\hline
284.375
\end{array}
$$

ANSWER Melissa drove 284.375 kilometers in all.

You can write a number sentence with decimal numbers and solve it to find the answer to the following story problem:

- Some of the campers drove 34.8 miles to see a waterfall. They saw a road sign every 6.96 miles. How many road signs did they see?

PROBLEM 3 Write a number sentence that you can use to solve this story problem.

SOLUTION

1. Read the problem.

2. Decide what question needs to be answered. For this problem, you need to find out how many road signs the campers saw if they saw a sign every 6.96 miles for 34.8 miles.

3. Decide what operation you need to use. For this problem, you need to use division to find the quotient of 34.8 divided by 6.96.

4. Write a number sentence that finds the quotient of 34.8 and the divisor 6.96.

ANSWER $34.8 \div 6.96 = ?$

PROBLEM 4 Solve the number sentence you wrote for Problem 3. Answer the question in a complete sentence.

SOLUTION

1. Write the number sentence that solves this problem. $\longrightarrow$ $34.8 \div 6.96 = ?$

2. Use the long-division symbol to write the problem. $\longrightarrow$ $6.96\overline{)34.8}$
   Use a step-by-step process to solve the problem.

3. Divide. You are dividing tenths by hundredths, so the answer is in tenths. $\longrightarrow$ $6.96\overline{)34.8} = 696\overline{)3480.0}$

$$\begin{array}{r} 5.0 \\ 696\overline{)3480.0} \\ -3480.0 \\ \hline 0 \end{array}$$

ANSWER The campers saw 5 road signs.

Write a multiplication or division number sentence. Solve.
Write the answer in a complete sentence.

1. It costs $42.95 to stay 1 night in a cabin at a campground. What is the cost of staying in the cabin for 5 nights?

2. Dean and his friends drove 37.3 kilometers each hour for 5.25 hours to get from the ranger station to the campsite by the lake. How many kilometers did Dean and his friends drive in all?

LEARN

3. The distance from the campsite to the lake is 0.6 of the distance from the campsite to the hiking trails. The distance from the campsite to the hiking trails is 1.4 kilometers. What is the distance from the campsite to the lake?

4. Ryan brought 6 bags of marshmallows to roast over a campfire. Each bag weighs 0.625 pound. How many pounds do the bags of marshmallows weigh in all?

5. Rick and his family spent 1.25 hours setting up their tent. They spent 1.04 as much time unpacking their camping supplies. How much time did Rick and his family spend unpacking their camping supplies?

6. A family packed 2.04 pounds of dried fruit for their camping trip. They ate the same amount of dried fruit on each of 3 days. How much dried fruit did they eat each day?

7. Ellen cooked veggie burgers over a campfire. She used 2.8 pounds of veggie mix to make the burgers. Each burger weighed 0.35 pound. How many veggie burgers did Ellen cook?

8. Campers hiked 8.82 miles in 4.2 hours. If they walked at the same speed for the entire hike, how many miles did they hike each hour?

9. Nick bought new lanterns for a camping trip. He spent a total of $37.45. Each lantern cost $7.49. How many lanterns did Nick buy?

10. Two families went on a canoe trip. They traveled 34.83 miles in 5.4 hours. If they paddled at the same speed for the entire canoe trip, how many miles did they travel each hour?

Numbers with Decimals

Use these numbers to answer Problems 1–3:
   four hundred fifty-three and one hundred five thousandths
   four hundred fifty-three and one hundred nine thousandths

1. Write the numbers as decimals and compare the numbers using $<$, $>$, or $=$. Explain your thinking.

2. Round each number to the nearest hundredth.

3. Compare the numbers rounded to hundredths using $<$, $>$, or $=$.

Solve.

4. Priscilla scored 15.47 points in the cooking competition. Michelle's score was 1.8 times as much as Priscilla's. Round each value to the nearest whole number to estimate Michelle's score.

    (a) Round each value to the nearest whole number.

    (b) Use the rounded values to estimate Michelle's score.

Think Like a Mathematician Self-Check

5. State the actions and thinking you used during this lesson as a math learner.

Math Thinking and Actions
I made sense of problems by • Explaining to myself what a problem means and what it asks for • Using drawings or diagrams to represent a problem I was solving
I explained my math thinking clearly.
I tried out new ways to check if an answer is reasonable.
Other

T R Y   I T

Evaluate Numerical Expressions

More Grouping Symbols

Worked Examples

Parentheses ( ), brackets [ ] and braces { } all serve the purpose of grouping items together in a certain way. In complicated expressions, the parentheses group items together at the innermost level, followed by brackets at the next level and braces at the outermost level.

Remember that the order of operations is always PEMDAS (Parentheses, Exponents, Multiplication or Division from left to right, and Addition or Subtraction from left to right). You can now also include brackets and braces along with parentheses as things you should simplify first in an expression. If all three types of grouping symbols are present, then expressions in parentheses should be simplified first, followed by those in brackets and then in braces. In other words, work from the inside out to remove grouping symbols.

One last important thing to know: If you have more than one operation within any type of grouping symbol, you always follow PEMDAS within that grouping symbol.

PROBLEM 1 Evaluate the expression.

$3 + \{[(4 + 6) - 7] - (1 + 2)\}$

SOLUTION

$$3 + \{[(4 + 6) - 7] - (1 + 2)\}$$
$$= 3 + \{[\quad 10 \quad - 7] - \quad 3 \quad \}$$
$$= 3 + \{\qquad 3 \quad - \quad 3 \quad \}$$
$$= 3 + \qquad\qquad 0$$
$$= \qquad\qquad\qquad 3$$

ANSWER 3

PROBLEM 2 Evaluate the expression.

$\{[(3+17)-4\cdot 2]-[9-(2\cdot 2)]\}-(2+2)$

SOLUTION Evaluate the expressions inside the parentheses first, then inside the brackets according to the order of operations, and then inside the braces.

$$
\begin{aligned}
&\{[(3+17)-4\cdot 2]-[9-(2\cdot 2)]\}-(2+2)\\
=&\{[\quad 20\quad -4\cdot 2]-[9-\quad 4\ ]\}-\quad 4\\
=&\{[\quad 20\quad -\ 8\ ]-\quad 5\quad \}-\quad 4\\
=&\{\qquad 12\qquad -\quad 5\quad \}-\quad 4\\
=&\qquad\qquad 7\qquad\qquad -\quad 4\\
=&\qquad\qquad\qquad\qquad 3
\end{aligned}
$$

ANSWER 3

Evaluate the expression.

1. $[(9-3)+2\cdot(3+4)]-[(5\cdot 3-5)+6]$

2. $\{[12-(2+1)]-4\cdot(3-1)\}+\{[7\cdot(5-3)]-(2+6)\}$

3. $\{24+[2\cdot(200-10^2)]\}+2\cdot(3+7)$

4. $2\cdot\{2+[3\cdot 7-3\cdot(10-5)]\}+4\cdot(1+2)$

LEARN

Create and Interpret Numerical Expressions

Create and Interpret Expressions

Translate the word phrase into a numerical expression.

1. the quotient of 6 divided by 12

2. 15 less than 30

3. the difference between 7 and 2

4. twice the sum of 6 and 4

5. 15 less than the product of 8 and 3

6. triple the quotient of 12 divided by 4

For the expression, describe the relationship among the numbers and symbols in two different ways.

7. $(12 - 6) \div 2$

8. $4 \cdot (13 + 7)$

TRY IT

One Variable in Algebraic Expressions

Use Substitution in Expressions

Worked Examples

You can substitute a number for a variable to evaluate an expression. This process is known as evaluating using substitution, or simply substitution.

PROBLEM 1 Find the value of this expression by substituting 2 for m:

$$19m$$

SOLUTION $19m = 19 \cdot 2$
$$= 38$$

Notice that this expression has one operation, multiplication. When 2 is substituted for the variable m, 19 is multiplied by 2.

ANSWER The value of the expression $19m$ is 38 when 2 is substituted for m.

PROBLEM 2 Find the value of this expression by substituting 2 for p:

$$7p + 8$$

SOLUTION $7p + 8 = 7 \cdot 2 + 8$
$$= 14 + 8$$
$$= 22$$

Notice that when 2 replaces p, the expression becomes $7 \cdot 2 + 8$. By the order of operations, the first step is to multiply, and the next step is to add.

ANSWER The value of the expression $7p + 8$ is 22 when 2 is substituted for p.

L E A R N

PROBLEM 3 Find the value of this expression by substituting 3 for n:

$$(5 + n) - 2$$

SOLUTION
$$
\begin{aligned}
(5 + n) - 2 &= (5 + 3) - 2 \\
&= 8 - 2 \\
&= 6
\end{aligned}
$$

Notice that the expression has two operations, addition and subtraction. The addition is in parentheses, so it is calculated first. Then the subtraction is calculated.

ANSWER The value of the expression $(5 + n) - 2$ is 6 when 3 is substituted for n.

PROBLEM 4 Find the value of this expression by substituting 4 for y:

$$8 \cdot 3 \div (2 + y)$$

SOLUTION
$$
\begin{aligned}
8 \cdot 3 \div (2 + y) &= 8 \cdot 3 \div (2 + 4) \\
&= 8 \cdot 3 \div 6 \\
&= 24 \div 6 \\
&= 4
\end{aligned}
$$

Notice that the expression has three operations, multiplication, division, and addition. The addition is calculated first because it is in parentheses. The multiplication is calculated second because the order of operations says to do multiplication and division from left to right. The division is calculated last because it is to the right of the multiplication.

ANSWER The value of the expression $8 \cdot 3 \div (2 + y)$ is 4 when 4 is substituted for y.

Find the value of the expression.

1. Substitute 25 for y.
   $6y$

2. Substitute 12 for g.
   $(27 - g) + 34$

3. Substitute 33 for k.
   $(22 + k) \div 5$

4. Substitute 7 for r.
   $(6 - 3) \cdot 5 + r$

5. Substitute 4 for d.
   $7 + 20 - (12 \div d)$

6. Substitute 12 for j.
   $(3 + j) \cdot 3 \div 9$

Expression and Equation Problems (A)

Expressions and Story Problems

Worked Examples

You can write an expression with a variable to represent a story problem.

PROBLEM Anna's mom buys 3 bags that contain an equal number of wrapped cheese slices. The number of cheese slices in each bag is not known. What expression describes the total number of cheese slices?

SOLUTION Divide to solve the problem. Use the method that is easiest for you. One way is shown below.

1 Identify what you know and what you don't know. You know that Anna's mom bought 3 bags. You know that each bag has an equal number of wrapped cheese slices. You don't know how many wrapped cheese slices are in each bag.

2 Name a variable, such as c, and decide what the variable stands for. You don't know the number of wrapped cheese slices in each bag, so the variable c stands for that unknown number.

3 Decide if you need to add, subtract, multiply, or divide. In this problem, you would multiply 3 times the number of cheese slices to get the answer.

ANSWER The expression is $3 \cdot c$. You can also write that expression as $3c$.

Write the expression for the story problem. You may decide what letter to use as a variable.

1. Percy earned $16 mowing lawns. He plans to spend part of that money at the county fair. What expression describes how much money he will have after he leaves the county fair?

2. Rochelle picked some peppers. Her neighbor gave her 15 more peppers. What expression describes how many peppers she has?

3. Terrence had some baseball cards. He wanted to divide them into 5 equal groups. What expression describes how many baseball cards will be in each group?

LEARN

Expression and Equation Problems (A)

Match Expressions and Story Problems

Worked Examples

You can show how an expression matches the details in the following story problem:

- Kim reads all the books her favorite author writes. On Wednesday, she checked out the author's newest book from the library and read 38 pages. On Thursday, she read more pages of the book. How many pages did Kim read in 2 days?

PROBLEM 1 What does the expression $38 + p$ mean in relation to the story problem?

SOLUTION

1 Figure out what p stands for in the expression. It represents the unknown number of pages Kim read on Thursday. You do not know what that number is yet.

2 Figure out what $38 + p$ means. It means 38 pages plus an unknown number of pages.

3 Use the expression in an explanation of how it relates to the story problem.

ANSWER The expression $38 + p$ represents the number of pages Kim read on Wednesday and Thursday.

Explain what the variable and numbers in the given expression mean. Then explain how the given expression is related to the story problem.

1. $5c \div 3$

   Larry washed cars for $5 each. He donated the money he earned equally to 3 groups that help students go to college. How much money did Larry donate to each group?

2. $b - 2$

   Inez is hiking on a park trail that is measured in miles. She has hiked 2 miles so far. How many miles does Inez have to hike until she completes the entire trail?

3. $12b$

   David removed all the books from 12 shelves. Each shelf had the same number of books on it. How many books did David remove from shelves?

You can write an expression to represent a story problem and then change the expression when the story problem changes.

- Bill brought an unknown number of baseball cards to a sports card show. He sold 7 baseball cards. What expression represents the number of baseball cards Bill has left?

PROBLEM 2 Write an expression for the story problem.

SOLUTION

1 Identify what you know. You know that Bill sold 7 baseball cards.

2 Identify what you don't know. You don't know how many baseball cards Bill brought to the sports card show. That unknown amount can be represented by the variable b.

3 Decide what operation you should use and write an expression with the variable b and the information you know.

ANSWER $b - 7$

PROBLEM 3 Extend Problem 1. What expression represents the number of baseball cards Bill has left if he sells 2 more cards?

SOLUTION

1 Add $7 + 2$ because he sold 7 cards and then 2 more cards.

2 Replace the 7 with a 9 in the expression.

ANSWER $b - 9$

PROBLEM 4 Caron had some milk boxes at home. She bought 4 more milk boxes. She could represent the number of milk boxes she has now by using the expression $m + 4$. What expression represents the number of milk boxes she has if she buys another 9 milk boxes?

SOLUTION

1 Write $4 + 9$ because you know that Caron bought 4 milk boxes and then 9 more milk boxes. Add.

$4 + 9 = 13$

2 Replace the 4 in the original expression, $m + 4$, with 13.

ANSWER $m + 13$

L E A R N

Explain what information you know and what information you don't know from reading the story problem. Then write an expression that represents the story problem.

4. Adam has 5 baskets and a pile of onions. He wants to put the same number of onions in each basket. What expression represents how many onions he should put in each basket?

Write an expression that represents the changed story problem.

5. Jerry has some ears of corn from his corn plants. He gave away 10 ears of corn. He could use the expression $c - 10$ for the amount of corn he gave away. If he then ate 3 ears of corn, what expression represents the number of ears of corn remaining?

6. A garden had some rows of beans. A deer ate 2 rows of beans. An expression that represents how many rows of beans were left is $g - 2$. If another deer ate 2 more rows of beans, what expression represents the number of rows of beans remaining?

LEARN

Expression and Equation Problems (A)

Practice with Expressions

Choose the answer.

1. Becky made beaded necklaces. She put 8 beads on each necklace. She could use the expression $8 \cdot n$ to represent the number of beads she used to make n necklaces.

   Which expression represents the number of beads Becky could use if she put 4 more beads on each necklace?

   A. $12 \cdot 4$ B. $8 \cdot 4$

   C. $4 \cdot n$ D. $12 \cdot n$

2. Randy bought several postcards when he was on vacation. He mailed 5 of the postcards to his friends. He could use the expression $p - 5$ to represent the number of postcards he has left.

   Which expression represents the number of postcards Randy has left if he sends 3 more postcards to friends?

   A. $p - 3$ B. $p - 8$

   C. $5 - 3$ D. $8 - 5$

3. Jennifer can do 6 fewer sit-ups than Michelle can. Jennifer described the number of sit-ups she can do using the expression $m - 6$.

   One day Jennifer was tired and did 2 fewer sit-ups than usual. Which expression represents the number of sit-ups Jennifer did that day?

   A. $6 - 2$ B. $m - 4$

   C. $m - 6$ D. $m - 8$

4. Beth bought 2 packages of coloring markers. She could use the expression $2m$ to represent the total number of coloring markers she bought.

   Which expression represents the total number of coloring markers Beth would have if she bought 5 more packages of coloring markers?

   A. 2×7 B. 2×5

   C. $7m$ D. $5m$

5. Pedro rented some movies on Saturday. He returned 1 movie on Monday. He could use the expression $m - 1$ to represent the number of movies he has left.

   Which expression represents the number of movies Pedro has left if he returns 2 more movies?

   A. $m - 2$ B. $m - 3$

   C. $3 - 2$ D. $2 - 1$

6. Jeffrey had some apples at home. He bought 6 more apples. He could represent the number of apples that he now has by using the expression $a + 6$.

   Which expression represents the number of apples Jeffrey has if he buys another 8 apples?

   A. $a + 6$ B. $a + 14$

   C. $6 + 8$ D. $6 + 14$

TRY IT

7. Megan worked 10 hours overtime in one month. She could use the expression $t + 10$ to represent the total time she worked.

   Which expression represents the total number of hours Megan worked if she had worked an additional 12 hours overtime?

   A. $t + 2$ B. $t + 10$

   C. $2 + 12$ D. $t + 22$

8. Peter has 4 fewer trophies than Jack. Peter can represent the number of trophies he has with the expression $t - 4$.

   Peter won another 2 trophies. Which expression represents the number of trophies Peter has now?

   A. $t - 2$ B. $t - 4$

   C. $t - 6$ D. $t - 10$

9. Carla had several jigsaw puzzles. She bought 6 more jigsaw puzzles. She could use the expression $p + 6$ to represent the number of jigsaw puzzles she has now.

   Which expression represents the number of jigsaw puzzles Carla has if she buys 4 more jigsaw puzzles?

   A. $10 + 4$ B. $p + 4$

   C. $6 + 4$ D. $p + 10$

10. Anna had some peaches at home. She bought 5 more peaches. She could represent the number of peaches that she now has by using the expression $p + 5$.

    Which expression represents the number of peaches Anna has if she buys another 3 peaches?

    A. $p + 3$ B. $p + 5$

    C. $p + 8$ D. $3 + 5$

11. Jason bought a number of packages of buns. There are 8 buns in each package. He could use the expression $8b$ to represent the number of buns he bought.

    Which expression would represent the number of buns Jason bought if the store had put an additional 2 buns into each package?

    A. 10×8 B. $2b$

    C. 2×8 D. $10b$

12. Edgar has a pack of stickers to share with his 4 friends. He could represent the number of stickers each friend would get using the expression $s \div 4$.

    Edgar is thinking of sharing his stickers with 1 additional friend. Which expression would represent the number of stickers each person would get now?

    A. $s \div 1$ B. $s \div 3$

    C. $s \div 5$ D. $4 + 1$

13. Paul paid $5 per ticket for a number of tickets to the baseball game on Wednesday. He could represent the total he spent on baseball tickets by using the expression $5t$.

    On Saturday, Paul bought the same number of tickets. However, the price of these tickets was $2 more per ticket. Which expression represents the amount Paul paid for tickets on Saturday?

    A. 5×2 B. $2t$

    C. $7t$ D. $10t$

14. Eddie has a set of football cards he wants to put in an album. He is planning on putting 9 cards per page. He could represent the number of pages he would need by using the expression $b \div 9$.

    Eddie is thinking of putting 5 fewer cards on each page. Which expression would represent the number of pages he would need?

    A. $b \div 4$ B. $b \div 5$

    C. $b \div 14$ D. $b \div 45$

TRY IT

Expression and Equation Problems (B)
Equations and Story Problems

Worked Examples

You can write an equation for a story problem.

PROBLEM A painter uses 2.5 gallons of paint to cover the walls in 1 room of a building. He needs to paint a total of 6 rooms in the building. Each room is the same size. What equation describes the number of gallons of paint the painter will need to finish the job?

SOLUTION Multiply to solve the problem. Use the method that is easiest for you. One way is shown below.

1 Identify what you know. You know that 2.5 gallons of paint are needed for 1 room. You know the painter will paint 6 rooms of equal size.

2 Identify what you don't know. You don't know the total number of gallons of paint needed to finish the job.

3 Name a variable, such as p, and decide what the variable stands for. You don't know the total number of gallons of paint needed, so the variable p stands for that unknown number.

4 Write an equation to show what the problem has told you. Because the painter is painting 6 rooms and needs 2.5 gallons of paint per room, you know you need to multiply. The variable will stand for the product.

ANSWER $2.5 \times 6 = p$, or $6 \times 2.5 = p$

Write an equation for the story problem. You may decide what letter to use as a variable.

1. Meredith used 54 seashells to decorate 6 picture frames. She put an equal number of seashells on each frame. What equation describes the number of seashells Meredith put on each picture frame?

2. Harry walked to the library and back home for a total of 1.25 miles. If he walks that route every day for 8 days, how many miles will he have walked?

L E A R N

Expression and Equation Problems (B)

Match Equations and Story Problems

Worked Examples

You can show how an equation matches the details in the following story problem:

* A scientist records data about wolves she is tracking. She knows there are 45 wolves in the area. She observes 22 of the wolves at a pond one day. The scientist wants to know how many wolves are not at the pond that day.

PROBLEM 1 How can $45 - w = 22$ be matched with the details in the story problem?

SOLUTION

1 Decide what w stands for in the equation. It stands for the unknown number of wolves that aren't at the pond that day.

2 Decide what $45 - w$ means. It means 45 minus an unknown number of wolves.

3 Decide what 22 means. It means the number of wolves the scientist observes at the pond.

ANSWER The equation $45 - w = 22$ represents the number of wolves that aren't at the pond that day.

Explain what the variable and numbers in the given equation mean.
Then explain how the given equation is related to the story problem.

1. $10 + 3c = 34$

   Linda had 10 comic books. She bought 3 boxes of comic books at a yard sale. Each box has the same number of comic books. Now Linda has 34 comic books. How many comic books are in each box?

2. $60 \div d = 3$

   Kelly bought 60 pounds of dry dog food. The dog food is in 3 equal-sized bags. How many pounds of dog food are in each bag?

Worked Examples

You can write an equation to represent a story problem and then change the equation when the story problem changes.

- Raul planted a flower garden. He planted 6 geraniums and 8 petunias in a row. How many flowers did Raul plant in a row?

PROBLEM 2 Write an equation for the story problem.

SOLUTION

1. Identify what you know. You know that Raul planted 6 geraniums and 8 petunias in a row.

2. Identify what you don't know. You don't know how many flowers Raul planted in a row. That unknown amount can be called variable f.

3. Decide which operation you should use, and write an equation with the variable f and the information you know.

ANSWER $6 + 8 = f$

PROBLEM 3 Extend the problem. What equation represents the total number of flowers Raul planted if he planted 3 rows that had 6 geraniums and 8 petunias in each row?

SOLUTION

1. Let the variable f represent the total number.

2. Show that $6 + 8$ is being multiplied by 3 by writing $3 \cdot (6 + 8)$.

3. Replace the expression $6 + 8$ with $3 \cdot (6 + 8)$ in the equation.

ANSWER $3 \cdot (6 + 8) = f$

PROBLEM 4 Sherman helped on park cleanup day and collected 9 pounds of cans and 6 pounds of bottles. He wrote this equation to represent the unknown total number of pounds of items he collected.

$9 + 6 = p$

He wanted to divide those items into 3 equal groups. Write an equation that represents the number of items in each group.

SOLUTION Show $9 + 6$ as an expression that is divided by 3.

ANSWER $(9 + 6) \div 3 = p$

LEARN

Explain what information you know and what information you don't know from reading the story problem. Then write an equation that represents the story problem.

3. Aisha wrote 12 poems during the summer. If she wrote 12 poems each in the fall, spring, and winter, how many poems did she write altogether?

Write an equation that represents the changed story problem.

4. Colton had 30 T-shirts and pairs of pants. He gave away 14 of those items that were too small. He wrote this equation to represent the items of clothing he gave away: $30 - 14 = c$.

    He then found another T-shirt and didn't give it away. What equation represents the total number of items of clothing he had after he gave away some items and found the T-shirt?

5. Annie had 17 notebooks and gave 5 of the notebooks to her sister. She wrote this equation to represent the number of notebooks she had left: $17 - 5 = n$.

    She decided to sort her notebooks into 3 stacks. What equation represents the number of notebooks in each stack?

Expression and Equation Problems (B)

Practice with Equations

Choose the answer.

1. Tara did 3 hours of math practice and 4 hours of social studies reading in 1 week. She wrote the following equation to represent the total number of hours, h, of practice and reading she did: $h = 3 + 4$.

   Tara expects to have 3 hours of math practice and 4 hours of social studies reading each week for the next 5 weeks. Now let the variable h represent the total number of hours of homework Tara will have. Which equation represents the total number of hours of work she will have in the next 5 weeks?

   A. $h = 3 + 4$ B. $h = 3 \times 4 \times 5$

   C. $h = 3 + 4 + 5$ D. $h = 5 \cdot (3 + 4)$

2. Tess made 6 corn muffins and 12 bran muffins. She wrote the following equation to represent the total number of muffins, m, she made: $m = 6 + 12$.

   Tess stores an equal number of the total number of muffins she made in each of 3 small containers. Now let the variable m stand for the number of muffins in each container. Which equation represents the number of muffins in each container?

   A. $m = 6 + 12 + 3$ B. $m = 6 + 12 - 3$

   C. $m = (6 + 12) \div 3$ D. $m = (6 + 12) \times 3$

3. Nathan always reads 2 more books than he is required to read in a month. He could show the total number of books he reads in a month with the expression $b + 2$, where b represents the number of books he is required to read.

   Which expression represents the total number of books Nathan read in a month if he read an additional 5 books more than required that month?

   A. $b + 2$ B. $2 + 5$

   C. $b + 7$ D. $2 + 3$

TRY IT

4. Maria planned to read 9 fiction and 12 history books each month. She could show the total number of books she planned to read each month with the equation $b = 9 + 12$, where b represents the number of books Maria planned to read.

Now let the variable b represent the total number of books Maria planned to read in 5 months. Which equation would represent the number of books Maria would read in 5 months?

A. $b = 5 + (9 + 12)$

B. $b = 5 \cdot (9 + 12)$

C. $b = 9 + 12 \cdot 5$

D. $b = 5 \cdot 9 + 12$

5. Ben had 15 stamps in his stamp collection. He sold 6 stamps. Ben wrote the following equation to represent the number of stamps he has left: $15 - 6 = t$. The variable t represents the total number of stamps Ben has left.

Ben bought 7 more stamps. Now let the variable t stand for the total number of stamps Ben has now. Which equation represents the number of stamps Ben has now?

A. $15 + 7 = t$

B. $15 - 6 + 7 = t$

C. $15 + 6 - 7 = t$

D. $15 \div 6 = t$

6. Pang weeded gardens for 2 hours on Friday. He wants to weed gardens for a total of 5 hours on Friday and Saturday. He wrote the following equation to describe the total number of hours he wants to weed gardens on Friday and Saturday: $2 + h = 5$.

The variable h represents the number of hours Pang will weed gardens on Saturday. Which situation does this equation describe?

A. Pang weeded gardens for 2 hours on Friday. He wasn't sure how many hours he would weed gardens on Saturday. He wants to weed gardens for a total of 5 hours on Friday and Saturday.

B. Pang weeded gardens for 2 hours on Friday. He weeded gardens for 5 hours on Saturday. He wasn't sure how many hours he would weed gardens on both Friday and Saturday.

C. Pang wasn't sure how many hours he would weed gardens on Friday. He wasn't sure how many hours he would weed gardens on Saturday. He wants to weed gardens for a total of 5 hours on Friday and Saturday.

D. Pang wasn't sure how many hours he would weed gardens on Friday. He weeded gardens for 5 hours on Saturday. He wants to weed gardens for a total of 5 hours on Friday and Saturday.

TRY IT

7. A farmer wants to plant a total of 80 stalks of corn. He plants 8 cornstalks in each row. He wrote the following equation to describe the number of rows of cornstalks he will plant: $80 = 8r$.

   The variable r represents the number of rows the farmer wants to plant. Which situation does this equation describe?

   A. A farmer wants to plant a total of 80 stalks of corn. He isn't sure how many rows of cornstalks he will plant. He isn't sure how many cornstalks he will plant in each row.

   B. A farmer wants to plant a total of 80 stalks of corn. He plants 72 rows of cornstalks. He isn't sure how many cornstalks he will plant in each row.

   C. A farmer wants to plant a total of 80 stalks of corn. He plants 8 cornstalks in each row. He isn't sure how many rows of cornstalks he will plant.

   D. A farmer wants to plant a total of 80 stalks of corn. He plants 8 cornstalks in each row. He will plant 8 rows of cornstalks.

8. April read 5 newspaper articles and 3 magazine articles every week. She wrote the following equation to represent the number of articles she read in a week: $r = 3 + 5$. The variable r represents the total number of articles April reads every week.

   Now let the variable r represent the total number of articles April reads in 6 weeks. Which equation would represent the total number of articles April would read in 6 weeks?

   A. $r = 6 + (3 + 5)$ B. $r = 3 + (6 \cdot 5)$ C. $r = (6 \cdot 3) + 5$ D. $r = 6 \cdot (3 + 5)$

9. Claudia bought some apples. She gave away 16 of them. She could represent the total number of apples she has left with the expression $a - 16$, where the variable a represents the total number of apples Claudia first bought.

   Claudia then gave away another 5 apples. Which expression represents the number of apples that Claudia has now?

   A. $16 - 5$ B. $a - 5$ C. $a - 16$ D. $a - 21$

10. Benny spends $3 a day on bus fare. He can represent the total amount he spends riding the bus with the expression $3b$, where b represents the number of days Benny rides the bus.

    The bus company is thinking of increasing the fares by $1 a day. Which expression would represent the amount Benny would spend at the new rate?

    A. $4b$ B. $12b$ C. 4×3 D. 1×3

T R Y   I T

11. Zoe sends letters to her pen pal by mail. She spends 42¢ on a stamp and 55¢ on an envelope. She wrote this equation to represent the total cost for sending a letter to her pen pal: $c = 42 + 55$. The variable c represents the total cost for sending a letter.

Zoe writes to her pen pal 8 times a year. Now let the variable c represent the total cost of sending her pen pals letters. Which equation would represent the total cost of sending her pen pal letters for a year?

A. $c = 8 + (42 + 55)$

B. $c = 42 + (8 \cdot 55)$

C. $c = 8 \cdot (42 + 55)$

D. $c = (8 \cdot 42) + 55$

12. Veronica had some cherries to give to 3 friends. She could represent the total number of cherries each friend would get with the expression $g \div 3$, where the variable g represents the total number of cherries Veronica has.

Veronica is thinking about giving cherries to 2 additional friends. Which expression represents the number of cherries each friend would now get?

A. $g \div 1$

B. $g \div 2$

C. $g \div 5$

D. $g \div 6$

13. Ms. Tania is planning the seating arrangements for her concert. She is dividing the seats equally into 6 rows. She could represent the total number of seats in each row with the expression $s \div 6$, where the variable s represents the total number of seats.

Ms. Tania is thinking about dividing all of the seats into 2 fewer rows than the original plan. Which expression would represent the number of seats in each row now?

A. $s \div 4$

B. $s \div 8$

C. $s \div 12$

D. $s \div 36$

14. John is planning the seating arrangements for the music show. He is dividing the total number of seats equally into 8 rows. He could represent the total number of seats in each row with the expression $t \div 8$, where the variable t represents the total number of seats.

John is thinking of dividing the seats into 2 more rows than the original plan. Which expression represents the total number of seats in each row now?

A. $t \div 6$

B. $t \div 10$

C. $t \div 16$

D. $8 + 2$

TRY IT

Expression and Equation Problems (C)

Write Story Problems

Worked Examples

You can write story problems about expressions and equations.

PROBLEM 1 There were an unknown number of people on a city bus. At the next stop, 8 people got off the bus.

This expression, with n representing the unknown number of people originally on the bus, can be written about the story problem:

$$n - 8$$

Write another story problem about this expression.

SOLUTION Figure out what the expression represents. The variable n represents an unknown number. Subtraction is the operation used, and 8 is subtracted from an unknown number.

ANSWER A number of bicycles were parked outside a bike rental shop. Riders came out from the shop and rode away on 8 bicycles.

PROBLEM 2 There are 72 cars in a parking lot. Each row has an equal number of cars. There are 9 rows of cars. How many cars are in each row?

This equation, with t representing the unknown number of cars in each row, can be written about the story problem:

$$72 \div t = 9$$

Write another story problem about this equation.

SOLUTION Figure out what the equation means. It starts with 72. The variable t is an unknown number that divides 72. The quotient is 9.

ANSWER There were 72 clean plates in the restaurant kitchen. The plates were stacked equally in 9 stacks. How many plates were in each stack?

PROBLEM 3 Write a story problem for this equation:

$$4 \cdot m = 36$$

SOLUTION Figure out what the equation means. The variable m represents an unknown number. When it is multiplied by 4, the product is 36.

ANSWER Mark, Maria, Annie, and Jake each brought the same number of sandwiches to a picnic. The 4 friends brought a total of 36 sandwiches to the picnic. How many sandwiches did each person bring?

L E A R N

Write a story problem for the expression or equation.

1. $6 + p$

2. $2a$

3. $b \div 4$

4. $f = 3 + 5$

5. $m - 4 = 6$

6. $18 = 6h$

Worked Examples

When a story problem changes, you can write a changed expression or changed equation.

PROBLEM 4 Andrea rode the bus for a number of miles. She then walked for 1.5 miles. She could represent the miles she traveled by the expression $b + 1.5$. The variable b represents the number of miles Andrea rode on the bus.

She then rode in a taxi for twice as many miles as she rode on the bus and she walked. Which expression represents the total number of miles she traveled by taxi?

In the new expression, let the variable b represent the original number of miles Andrea rode on the bus.

SOLUTION Start with the expression from the original problem. Figure out how to represent *twice as many* from the changed story problem. For *twice as many*, multiply by 2.

ANSWER $2 \cdot (b + 1.5)$

PROBLEM 5 Chip hiked on a lakeside trail for 3 miles. He then hiked up a mountain trail for 2 miles. He could represent the total miles he hiked with the variable m in the equation $3 + 2 = m$.

What equation would represent the miles he hiked if he then hiked down the mountain trail for 2 miles?

In the new equation, let the variable m represent the total miles hiked on the trail and up and down the mountain.

SOLUTION Start with the equation from the original problem. Figure out how to represent an additional 2 miles from the changed story problem. For an additional 2 miles, add 2.

ANSWER $3 + 2 + 2 = m$

LEARN

Write a changed expression or changed equation.

7. Marty had checked out 7 books from the library. He returned 3 of the books. He could represent the books he still had with the variable p in the equation $7 - 3 = p$. If he then checked out 6 more books, what equation would represent how many books he had? In the new equation, let the variable p represent the total number of books Marty had after he checked out 6 more books.

8. Annette planted 20 sunflower seeds and some watermelon seeds. She could represent the number of seeds she planted with the expression $20 + w$, where w represents the number of watermelon seeds Annette planted. If Annette planted 4 times as many of the same seeds the next day, what expression would represent the number of seeds she planted on that day? In the new expression, let the variable w represent the number of watermelon seeds Annette originally planted.

9. On Monday, Wendi collected 28 grass samples for a science project. The next day, she collected 8 more grass samples. She could represent the number of grass samples she collected with the variable g in the equation $28 + 8 = g$. If she then discarded 4 grass samples, what equation would represent the number of grass samples she had? In the new equation, let the variable g represent the total number of grass samples Wendi had after she discarded 4 samples.

LEARN

Work with Numerical Expressions

For each problem:

(a) Determine the value of the expression as given.

(b) Insert grouping symbols to create a true equation with the new given value. (Hint: More than one set of grouping symbols may be required.)

(c) Show each step of the order of operations process to prove that the equation you created in Part (b) is true.

1. $3 \cdot 14 - 4 \div 2 + 10^2 \cdot 3 = ?$ New value: 315

2. $14 + 2 \cdot 3 - 12 \div 6 - 2 = ?$ New value: 45

3. Evaluate the expression. Express your answer in decimal form.

   $$72.5 + \left(\frac{2}{3} - \frac{1}{6}\right) \cdot \frac{1}{2} - 14.25 \div (0.03 + 0.22)$$

For each problem:

(a) Translate the word phrase into a mathematical expression.

(b) Evaluate the expression. Express fractions in simplest terms.

4. the product of five-twelfths and the sum of seven-fifteenths and one-third

5. double the sum of twenty-one and six-tenths and forty-three and seven-hundredths

TRY IT

6. State the actions and thinking you used during this lesson as a math learner.

Math Thinking and Actions
I made sense of problems by • Explaining to myself what a problem means and what it asks for • Using drawings or diagrams to represent a problem I was solving
I explained my math thinking clearly.
I tried out new ways to check if an answer is reasonable.
Other

TRY IT

The Coordinate Plane

Coordinate Plane Practice

Name the parts of the coordinate plane.

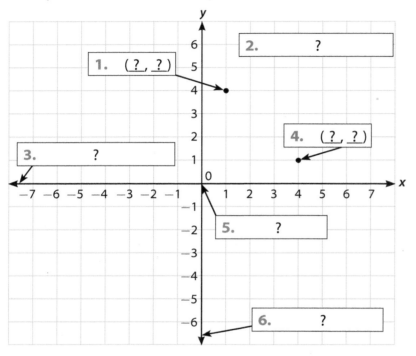

1. (? , ?)
2. ?
3. ?
4. (? , ?)
5. ?
6. ?

Use this grid and the Coordinate Graphs printout to solve.

7. Plot the location given and label it with the name of the building.

   (a) bike shop (4, 3)

   (b) Jon's house (9, 7)

8. Jon walked from his house directly toward the library and his friend walked directly from the bike shop toward the gas station. Their paths intersected at the grocery store. Plot and label the grocery store on the graph.

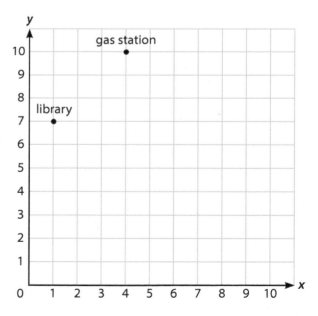

9. Each square on the graph represents a city block. Jon rode his bike straight to the grocery store and then straight to the bike shop. Write and use the distance formula to determine how many blocks he rode. Show all work.

10. The card shop forms a rectangle with Jon's house, the grocery store, and the bike shop. What are the coordinates of the card shop? Explain.

TRY IT

Ordered Pairs

Interpret Coordinates on a Graph

Worked Examples

You can describe what ordered pairs mean. You can explain what a graph means.

PROBLEM Stephen decided to collect 6 pieces of recyclable items every week. He wants to make a graph so he can predict the total amount of recyclable items he will pick up after 4 weeks. Create a graph with the following points to show how much he will pick up. Then interpret the points on the graph.

- W (1, 6)
- X (2, 12)
- Y (3, 18)
- Z (4, 24)

SOLUTION

1 Plot each point on a coordinate grid.

2 Interpret the graph:
- Explain what each ordered pair means.
- Explain whether or not a line should connect the points.
- Explain whether any of the ordered pairs can have a number less than or equal to 0 as a coordinate.
- Explain how seeing the graph makes it easier to understand what is happening in the story problem.

ANSWER

Stephen's Recycling Goals

Interpretation of the graph:

- *W* (1, 6) means that in the first week, Stephen picked up a total of 6 recyclable items.

  X (2, 12) means that in the second week, he picked up a total of 12 recyclable items.

  Y (3, 18) means that in the third week, he picked up a total of 18 recyclable items.

  Z (4, 24) means that in the fourth week, he picked up a total of 24 recyclable items.

- A line should not connect the points. It does not make sense in the problem to talk about the number of recycled items Stephen collects in $1\frac{1}{2}$ or $2\frac{1}{2}$ weeks.

- None of the ordered pairs should have a number less than or equal to 0 as a coordinate because 0 or fewer weeks and 0 or fewer recyclable items are not possible in this problem.

- It helps to see that as the number of weeks increases, the number of recyclable items increases.

Plot the points on a Quadrant I Coordinate Grid.

1. Paul collects baseball cards. Each pack has 5 cards. Paul decides to make a graph so that he can keep track of how many cards he has. Plot the points and ordered pairs with their labels.

   - *A* (0, 0)
   - *B* (1, 5)
   - *C* (2, 10)
   - *D* (3, 15)

Number of Packs and Baseball Cards

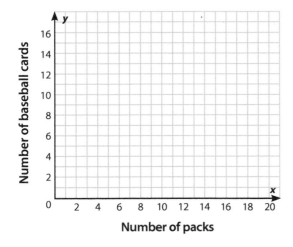

Refer to the story problem and the points, ordered pairs, and labels you plotted in Problem 1 to answer the following questions.

2. What does the ordered pair (0, 0) mean?

3. What does the ordered pair (1, 5) mean?

4. What does the ordered pair (2, 10) mean?

5. What does the ordered pair (3, 15) mean?

6. Can there be a negative number of baseball card packs?

7. Can there be a negative number of baseball cards?

8. What happens to the number of baseball cards as the number of packs increase?

9. What happens to the graph as the number of packs increases and the number of cards increases?

10. Does it make sense to connect the points in the graph with a line? Why?

11. How does seeing the graph make it easier to understand what is happening in the situation?

LEARN

Ordered Pairs

Practice to Understand Coordinates

Plot the points on a Quadrant I Coordinate Grid.

1. Tim's family went on vacation to Yellowstone National Park. When they left, they had 15 gallons of gas. After 1 hour, they had 12 gallons of gas left. Tim made a graph of how much gas they had left after each hour so his mother could plan when she would need to stop for gas. Plot the following points, ordered pairs, and labels, and connect the points with a line:

   - *A* (0, 15)
   - *B* (1, 12)
   - *C* (2, 9)
   - *D* (3, 6)
   - *E* (4, 3)
   - *F* (5, 0)

Amount of Gas and Travel Time

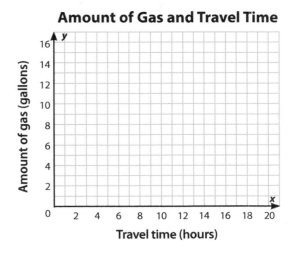

Refer to the story problem and the points, ordered pairs, and labels you plotted in Problem 1 to answer the following questions.

2. What does the ordered pair (0, 15) mean?

3. What does the ordered pair (1, 12) mean?

4. What does the ordered pair (2, 9) mean?

5. What does the ordered pair (3, 6) mean?

6. What does the ordered pair (4, 3) mean?

7. What does the ordered pair (5, 0) mean?

8. What happens to the hours as the gallons of gas decrease?

T R Y   I T

Choose the answer.

9. Ben's graph shows that the total number of medals won by Team USA on day 3 was 8. How many medals were won by day 5?

   A. 2   B. 5

   C. 11   D. 15

Team USA Medals Won

10. Frankie kept track of the goals scored by his soccer team. Frankie's graph shows that after 2 games his team had scored 5 goals. How many games did it take to score 9 goals?

    A. 3   B. 6

    C. 9   D. 13

Goals Scored in Games

11. Patrice's graph shows that the total rainfall after 3 hours was 5 centimeters. How much rain fell from the second hour to the sixth hour?

    A. 3 cm   B. 4 cm

    C. 6 cm   D. 7 cm

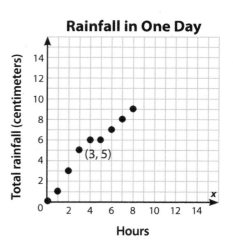

Rainfall in One Day

TRY IT

Graph or Write an Equation (A)

Equations and Function Tables

Worked Examples

You can use the equation for a function table to complete the table, just as you can use the rule for an input-output table to complete the table.

PROBLEM Explain what a function and a function table are. Complete a function table.

SOLUTION Below are an input-output table and a function table. By comparing the two tables, you can learn what a function table is.

- Both tables have an input column on the left. In function tables, the input column is named for a variable, such as x.
- Both tables have an output column on the right. In function tables, the output column is named for a variable, such as y.
- Both tables have a rule at the top, but in function tables, the rule is written as an equation and is called the function rule.
- In a function table, when you need to find a value, substitute the known value of either variable (whichever one you know) into the equation to get the value of the other variable. In an input-output table, use the rule and the known input or output to get the answer.

Input-Output Table Rule: Add 5		Function Table $y = x + 5$	
Input	**Output**	**x**	**y**
5	10	5	10
6	11	6	11
7	?	7	?
?	13	?	13
9	14	9	14
10	?	10	?

LEARN

A function is an equation that you can use to find the value of variables. In a function, put the value of a variable, such as *x*, into the equation. Then solve for the other variable, such as *y*. A function table is a table that lists input values and output values for a function rule.

To complete this table, substitute the values for *x* or *y* into the function to solve for the unknown values.

$y = x + 5$	
x	y
5	10
6	11
7	12
8	13
9	14
10	15

Complete the function table.

1.

$y = 2x$	
x	y
3	?
4	?
5	?
6	?
7	?
8	?
9	?
10	?
11	?
12	?

2.

$y = x - 2$	
x	y
2	?
3	?
4	?
5	?
6	?
7	?
8	?
9	?
10	?
11	?

3.

y = x + 4	
x	y
10	?
11	?
12	?
?	?
14	18
?	?
16	?
17	?

4.

y = 3x	
x	y
1	?
2	?
3	?
?	15
8	?
?	30
12	?

L E A R N

Graph or Write an Equation (A)

Find Equations for Function Tables

You can identify the equation that matches the *x*-values and *y*-values in a function table.

PROBLEM 1 Which of these two equations matches the values in the function table?

$y = x + 2$ or $y = 3x$

SOLUTION

	?
x	*y*
1	3
2	6
3	9

1 Substitute the *x*- and *y*-values into each equation, starting with the values in the first row.

2 Start with $y = x + 2$. Substitute 1 for *x* and 3 for *y* in that equation. Then substitute 1 for *x* and 3 for *y* in $y = 3x$.

The equations are true when the values of 1 and 3 from the function table are substituted for *x* and *y*.

$y = x + 2$	
x	*y*
1	3

It is true that
$3 = 1 + 2$.

$y = 3x$	
x	*y*
1	3

It is true that
$3 = 3(1)$.

3 Substitute the values in the second row into each equation.

Only the equation $y = 3x$ is true when 2 and 6 are substituted for *x* and *y*.

$y = x + 2$	
x	*y*
1	3
2	6

It is **not** true that
$6 = 2 + 2$.

$y = 3x$	
x	*y*
1	3
2	6

It is true that
$6 = 3(2)$.

4 Check the rest of the values in the function table to make sure the equation is true for those values.

Since $9 = 3(3)$, $y = 3x$ is true for all values in the function table.

ANSWER The equation $y = 3x$ matches the values in the function table.

$y = 3x$	
x	y
1	3
2	6
3	9

PROBLEM 2 Which equation matches the function table?

SOLUTION

1 Look carefully at all the x- and y-values in the function table.

2 Note that each y-value is greater than the x-value on the same row. That fact helps you know which operation is used in the function. Because the y-value is greater than the x-value in each row, the equation that matches the function table must use either addition or multiplication.

3 Note that the y-value increases by 1 in all rows of the function table. Because it increases by 1, "+ 1" might be in the equation.

4 Try $y = x + 1$ as the equation that matches the function table. When you substitute 1 for x and 2 for y, the equation is true. Substitute the rest of the values into the equation.

5 When you substitute the values in each row of the function table in the equation $y = x + 1$, find that the following equations are true:

$2 = 1 + 1$ $3 = 2 + 1$ $4 = 3 + 1$

$5 = 4 + 1$ $6 = 5 + 1$ $7 = 6 + 1$

ANSWER The equation that matches the function table is $y = x + 1$.

?	
x	y
1	2
2	3
3	4
4	5
5	6
6	7

$y = x + 1$	
x	y
1	2
2	3
3	4
4	5
5	6
6	7

LEARN

Choose the equation for the function table.

1.

?	
x	**y**
0	4
1	5
2	6
3	7
4	8
5	9
6	10

A. $y = x + 4$

B. $y = 2x$

2.

?	
x	**y**
0	0
1	1
2	2
3	3
4	4
5	5
6	6

A. $y = x - 2$

B. $y = x$

Write the equation that matches the function table.

3.

?	
x	**y**
1	0
2	1
3	2
4	3
5	4
6	5

LEARN

Graph or Write an Equation (B)

Find an Equation Used to Make a Graph

Worked Examples

You can use the coordinates of points on the graph of a line to complete a function table. You can use the function table to find the linear equation for the graph.

PROBLEM   Use the graph to complete the function table. Find the equation that was used to create the graph.

Linear Function

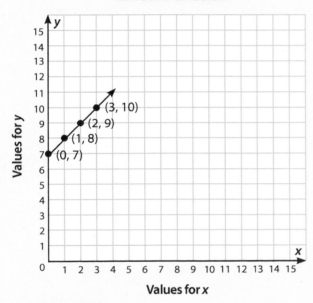

?	
x	*y*
?	?
?	?
?	?
?	?

Values for *x*

SOLUTION

1   Use the ordered pairs from the graph to complete the function table.

- Ordered pair (0, 7) has 0 for the *x*-coordinate and 7 for the *y*-coordinate. Write 0 in the first row of the table in the *x* column. Write 7 in the first row in the *y* column.

- Ordered pair (1, 8) has 1 for the *x*-coordinate and 8 for the *y*-coordinate. Write 1 in the second row of the table in the *x* column. Write 8 in that row in the *y* column.

L E A R N

- Ordered pair (2, 9) has 2 for the *x*-coordinate and 9 for the *y*-coordinate. Write 2 in the third row of the table in the *x* column. Write 9 in that row in the *y* column.
- Ordered pair (3, 10) has 3 for the *x*-coordinate and 10 for the *y*-coordinate. Write 3 in the fourth row of the table in the *x* column. Write 10 in that row in the *y* column.

2 Figure out the pattern of the *x*- and *y*-values in the function table.
- Each ordered pair has a *y*-value that is 7 more than the *x*-value. Because the *y*-values are greater than the *x*-values, consider using addition or multiplication of the *x*-values.
- Using information shown in the function table, see if $y = x + 7$ would work as the equation. Substitute each *x*- and *y*-value into $y = x + 7$.
- The equation is true for all the *x*- and *y*-values in the function table.

ANSWER The equation $y = x + 7$ was used to create the graph.

$y = x + 7$	
x	*y*
0	7
1	8
2	9
3	10

LEARN

Use the graph to complete the function table.
Write the equation for the graph.

1.

Linear Function

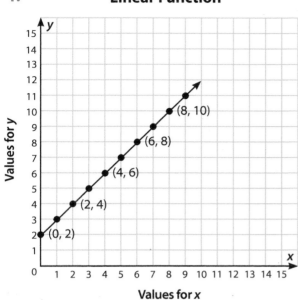

?	
?	?
?	?
?	?
?	?
?	?
?	?
?	?
?	?
?	?
?	?
?	?

2.

Linear Function

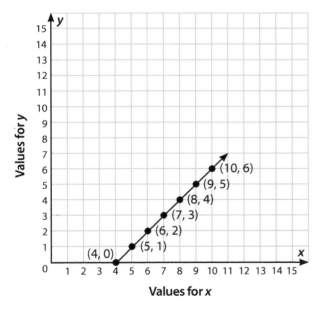

?	
?	?
?	?
?	?
?	?
?	?
?	?
?	?

LEARN

Graph or Write an Equation (B)

Practice Function Tables and Graphs

Use the graph to complete a function table.
Write the equation for the graph.

1.

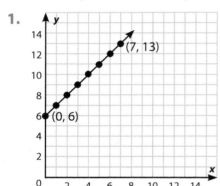

?	
x	**y**
?	?
?	?
?	?
?	?
?	?
?	?
?	?
?	?

TRY IT

Choose the graph that matches the equation.

2. $y = x + 2$

A.
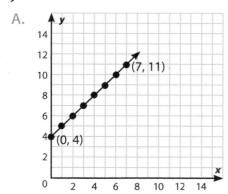

B.
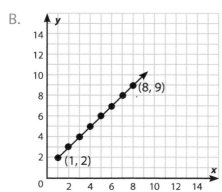

C.
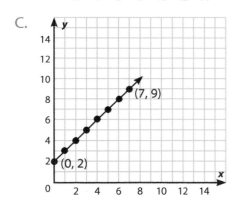

3. $y = x + 4$

A.
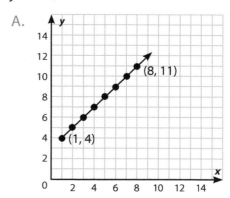

B.
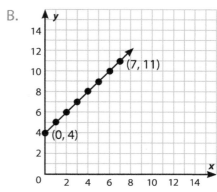

C.
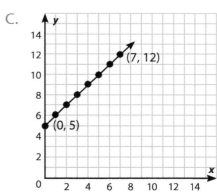

TRY IT

Choose the graph that matches the equation.

4. $y = x + 5$

A.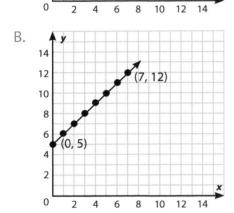

B.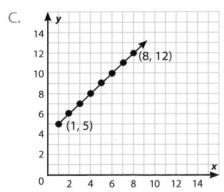

C.

5. $y = x + 1$

A.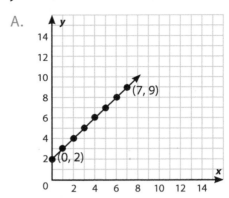

B.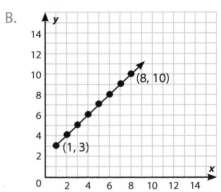

C.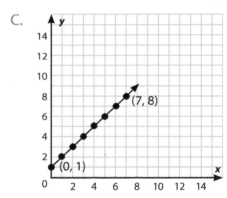

TRY IT

6. $y = 2x$

A.

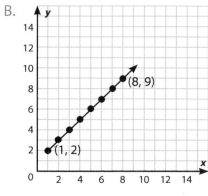

B.

C.

7. $y = 4x$

A.

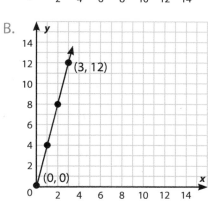

B.

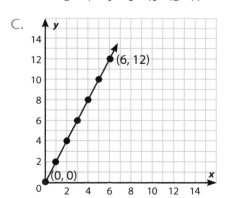

C.

TRY IT

Choose the equation that could have been used to create the graph.

8.

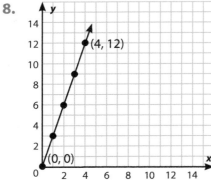

A. $y = x + 3$ B. $y = 3x$

C. $y = x + 0$ D. $y = x + 2$

9.

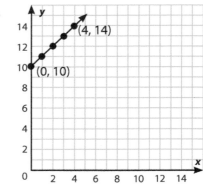

A. $y = 10x$ B. $y = x + 10$

C. $y = x + 0$ D. $y = x + 8$

10.

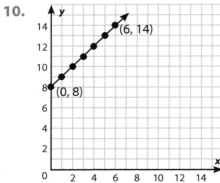

A. $y = x + 8$ B. $y = x + 1$

C. $y = 8x$ D. $y = x + 0$

11.

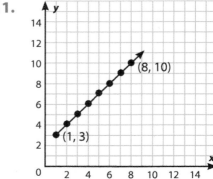

A. $y = x + 3$ B. $y = 2x$

C. $y = x + 0$ D. $y = x + 2$

TRY IT

Graph or Write an Equation (C)

Graph Equations About Animals

Worked Examples

You can create a function table and a graph to show data from a story problem about an animal.

PROBLEM   A tortoise walked 5 meters in 1 minute. How many meters would the tortoise walk in 2 minutes? In 3 minutes? In 4 minutes? In 5 minutes?

Create a function table with the data. Plot the data on a graph.

SOLUTION

1 Decide what variables will represent the data. Use m for the number of minutes. Use r for the number of meters the tortoise walks. In the function table, put m at the top of the left-hand column and r at the top of the right-hand column.

2 Fill in the values for the number of minutes (m) in the function table. The m column will show 1, 2, 3, 4, and 5.

3 Note that the number of meters (r) the tortoise walked in 1 minute was 5, so the number of meters the tortoise walks in 2 minutes would be 5×2. The product is 10, so a 10 is placed in row 2 in the r column. Find the number of meters for the rest of the r column by multiplying 5 by each value for m.

4 Find the equation that represents the relationship between r and m. The number of minutes times 5 equals the number of meters walked, so the equation that represents the values in the function table is $r = 5m$. Write the equation at the top of the function table.

5 Write a title for the coordinate grid. Label the axes and the units. The horizontal axis will represent the minutes that the tortoise walks. Label the units 1, 2, 3, 4, and 5. The vertical axis will represent the number of meters walked. Label the units 5, 10, 15, 20, and 25. The vertical axis could be labeled in ones, but it would make that axis much longer than the horizontal axis.

6 Plot the points by using the values in the function table.

(1, 5)   (2, 10)   (3, 15)   (4, 20)   (5, 25)

L E A R N

r = 5m	
m	**r**
1	5
2	10
3	15
4	20
5	25

Meters Walked by Tortoise Over Time

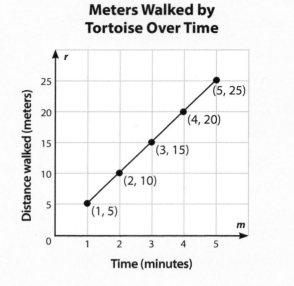

Use the data from the story problem to create a function table.
Then plot the data on the graph.

1. A koala sleeps for about 14 hours every day. How many hours of sleep does a koala get in 2 days? In 3 days? In 4 days? In 5 days?

?	
?	**?**
1	?
2	28
3	?
4	?
5	?

Koala Sleep Totals Over Time

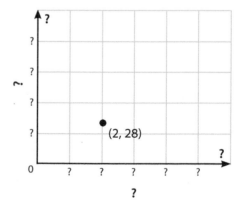

Graph or Write an Equation (C)

Practice with Graphs of Equations

Choose the graph that matches the story problem.

1. Carla is selling hot dogs. Each hot dog she sells comes with 4 pickles. Which graph shows the number of pickles served if Carla sells *h* hot dogs?

   A.

   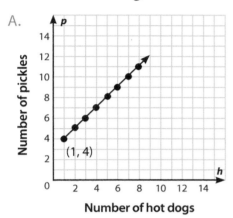

   Number of hot dogs

   B.

   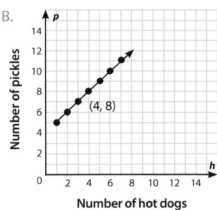

   Number of hot dogs

   C.

   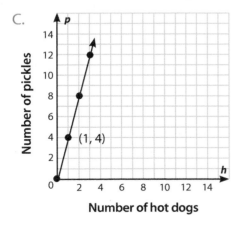

   Number of hot dogs

2. Danny is running for charity. He raises $5 for each mile he runs. Which graph shows the amount Danny will raise if he runs for *m* miles?

   A.

   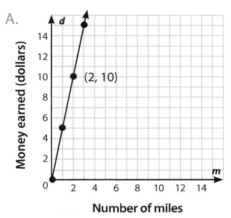

   Number of miles

   B.

   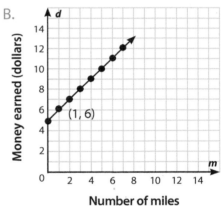

   Number of miles

   C.

   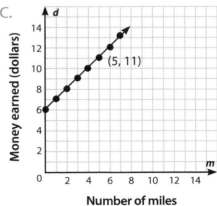

   Number of miles

T R Y   I T

Choose the graph that matches the story problem.

3. At the Dandelion Café, each milkshake comes with 2 straws. Which graph shows the number of straws the café will use if it serves *m* milkshakes?

A.

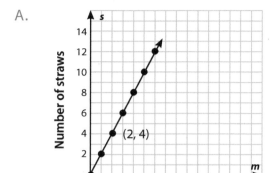

Number of milkshakes

B.

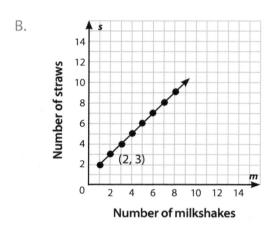

Number of milkshakes

C.

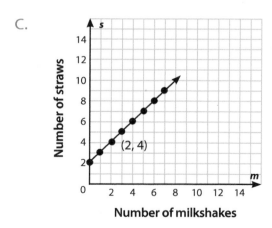

Number of milkshakes

4. Tommy is paid $7 per hour for raking the leaves. Which graph shows the amount Tommy will earn if he rakes leaves for *h* hours?

A.

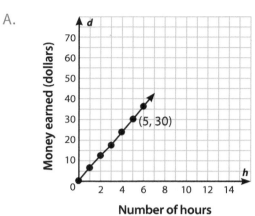

Number of hours

B.

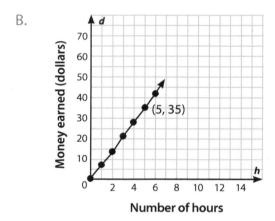

Number of hours

C.

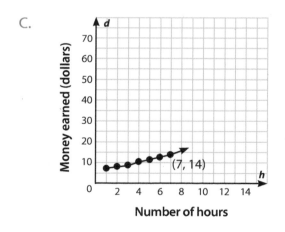

Number of hours

TRY IT

5. Penny charges $3 for each silk flower she makes. Which graph shows the amount Penny will earn if she makes f silk flowers?

A.
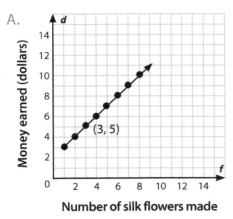
Number of silk flowers made

B.
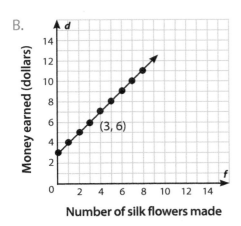
Number of silk flowers made

C.
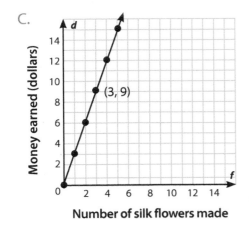
Number of silk flowers made

Choose the equation that matches the story problem.

6. Bobby earns $5 for every car he washes. Which equation shows the amount Bobby will earn if he washes c cars? (Use t to represent the total money earned and c to represent the number of cars washed.)

A. $t = c + 5$ B. $t = c - 5$

C. $t = 5c$ D. $t = c \div 5$

7. Sarah is paid $7 an hour for raking the leaves. Which equation shows the amount Sarah will earn if she rakes leaves for h hours? (Use t to represent the total money earned and h to represent the number of hours.)

A. $t = 7 + h$ B. $t = 7h$

C. $t = 7 \div h$ D. $t = 7 - h$

8. Each shirt in the store has 6 buttons. Which equation shows the number of buttons there are on r shirts? (Use t to represent the total number of buttons and r to represent the number of shirts.)

A. $t = 6r$ B. $t = 6 + r$

C. $t = 6 - r$ D. $t = 6 \div r$

9. Tanya rides her bike 5 miles in an hour. Which equation shows the number of miles Tanya will ride in g hours? (Use w to represent the total number of miles and g to represent the number of hours.)

A. $w = 5 + g$ B. $w = 5 - g$

C. $w = 5 \div g$ D. $w = 5g$

TRY IT

Graph or Write an Equation (D)

Graph Equations About Purchases

Worked Examples

You can solve a story problem with decimal numbers by creating a function table, writing a two-step equation, and drawing a line graph.

PROBLEM Daniella bought 1 loaf of bread for $2.00. She also bought 4 bags of vegetables for $2.50 each. How much was her total purchase?

Also, figure out the total cost if she had purchased 5, 6, or 7 bags of vegetables.

Use the data from the story problem to complete a function table, write a two-step equation, and plot the data on the graph. Then answer the question for 4 bags of vegetables and 1 loaf of bread.

SOLUTION

1 Select the variables that will represent the data. Use v for the number of bags of vegetables Daniella selected. Use d for the amount in dollars of her purchase. In the function table, put v at the top of the left-hand column. Put d at the top of the right-hand column.

2 Figure out which variable depends on the other one. The variable d depends on the variable v because the number of dollars spent on bread and vegetables depends on the number of bags of vegetables purchased.

3 In the left column of the function table, list the values for v: 4, 5, 6, and 7.

4 Figure out what two operations the equation will have.
- multiplication: The amount $2.50 must be multiplied by the number of bags of vegetables.
- addition: The amount $2.00 must be added for the cost of the loaf of bread.

5 Write the equation $d = 2.5v + 2$ at the top of the function table.

6 Substitute each value for v into the equation and solve for d. Put the values for d in the right column of the function table.

7 Use the values in the function table as coordinates. Plot the points. Do not connect the points with a line. The data between the points wouldn't make sense for this story problem because Daniella cannot buy, for example, a half loaf of bread or a half bag of vegetables.

8 Give the graph a title.

$d = 2.5v + 2$	
v	d
4	12
5	14.5
6	17
7	19.5

Daniella paid $12.00 for 4 bags of vegetables and 1 loaf of bread.

Costs of Grocery Purchases

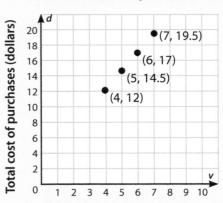

Number of bags of vegetables

Use the data from the story problem to complete a function table, write a two-step equation, and plot the data on the Graphing Equations printout. Then answer the question.

1. Ralph set up a lemonade stand at a soccer game. He sold jumbo cups of lemonade for $1.50 each. The total cost of supplies for the lemonade stand was $9. Ralph sold 11 jumbo cups of lemonade as soon as the stand opened. How much profit did he make?

?	
?	?
?	?
?	?
?	?
?	?
?	?
?	?
?	?

Cups of Lemonade Sold and Profit

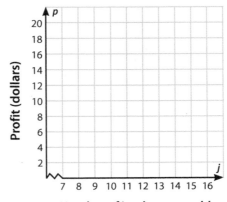

Number of jumbo cups sold

LEARN

Graph or Write an Equation (D)

Graph Two-Step Equations

Choose the graph that matches the story problem.

1. Annie is saving money. Her dad said that whatever she saves, he will give her $5 more. Which graph shows the amount Annie will have if she saves *v* dollars?

   A.
   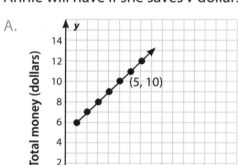
   Annie's savings (dollars)

   B.
   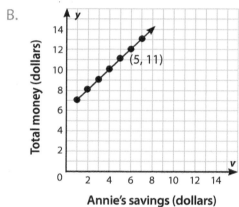
   Annie's savings (dollars)

   C.
   Annie's savings (dollars)

2. Gerald is saving money. His mom said that whatever he saves, she will give him $10 more. Which graph shows the amount Gerald will have if he saves *d* dollars?

   A.
   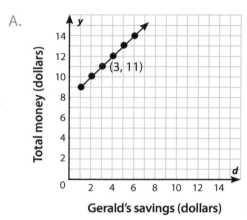
   Gerald's savings (dollars)

   B.
   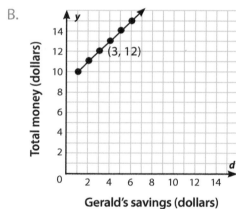
   Gerald's savings (dollars)

   C.
   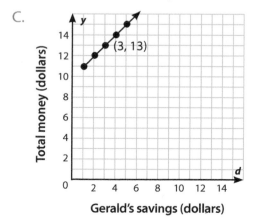
   Gerald's savings (dollars)

3. Taz is running for charity. He gets $1 for each mile he runs and a fixed amount of $12. Which graph shows how much Taz will raise if he runs for *p* miles?

A.

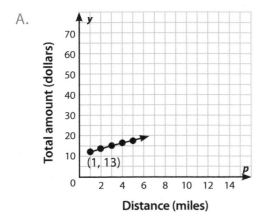

B.

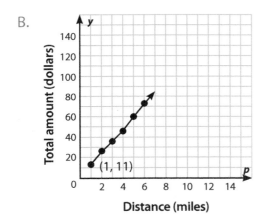

C.

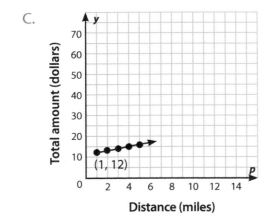

4. Raquel is collecting magazines to recycle. She gets $1 per pound and another $7 for taking the whole amount to the recycling facility. Which graph shows how many dollars Raquel will earn if she drops off *k* pounds of magazines?

A.

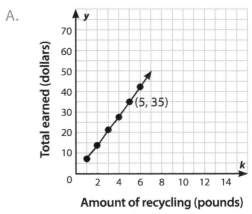

B.

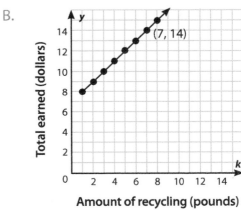

C.

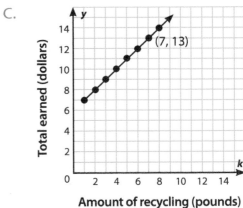

TRY IT

Choose the equation that solves the problem.

5. Harry made 8 pennants on Monday. He plans to make a number of pennants on Tuesday. Which equation shows the total number of pennants Harry will make in 2 days? (Use w to represent the total number of pennants and x to represent the number of pennants made on Tuesday.)

A. $w = x - 8$

B. $w = x + 8$

C. $w = x \div 8$

D. $w = 8x$

6. Heidi saved $4 last month. She plans to save more money this month. Which equation shows the total amount Heidi will save in 2 months? (Use m to represent the total amount of money Heidi will save and d to represent the total amount she saves the second month.)

A. $m = d \div 4$

B. $m = d - 4$

C. $m = d + 4$

D. $m = 4d$

7. Xavier recycled 30 pounds of paper last year. He plans to continue to recycle this year. Which equation shows how much paper Xavier will recycle in 2 years? (Use t to represent the total amount recycled in 2 years and q to represent the amount recycled this year.)

A. $t = 30 - q$

B. $t = 30q$

C. $t = 30 + q$

D. $t = 30 \div q$

TRY IT

Worked Examples

You can make a graph to compare two number patterns.

PROBLEM Complete each function table using the same set of input values. For the input values that are missing, choose your own values. For each table, graph the ordered pairs formed by each input and output and draw a ray through the points. Then compare the graphs.

Rule: Add 6	
Input	Output
0	?
1	?
?	?
8	?
?	?

Rule: Add 2	
Input	Output
0	?
1	?
?	?
8	?
?	?

ANSWER

1 To complete each function table, first complete the input values. (In this example, input values of 4 and 10 were chosen for the missing input values. Different values could have been chosen.) Then apply the rule to each input value to get the output values.

Rule: Add 6	
Input	Output
0	6
1	7
4	10
8	14
10	16

Rule: Add 2	
Input	Output
0	2
1	3
4	6
8	10
10	12

L E A R N

2 Rewrite each set of input and output values as ordered pairs.

Add 6: {(0, 6), (1, 7), (4, 10), (8, 14), (10, 16)}

Add 2: {(0, 2), (1, 3), (4, 6), (8, 10), (10, 12)}

3 Graph each set of ordered pairs on the same coordinate plane. Then draw a ray through each set of ordered pairs.

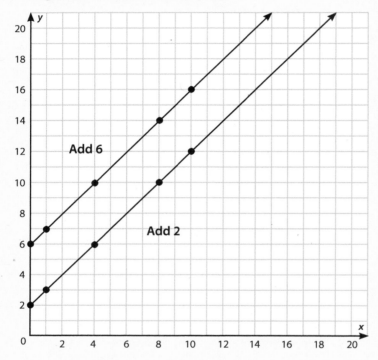

4 Compare the graphs. The output values, or y-values, of each graph increase as the input values, or x-values, increase. The rays are parallel. The graphs both increase at the same rate. However, the output values in the graph of "Add 6" are all 4 greater than the output values in the graph of "Add 2."

LEARN

Complete each function table using the same set of input values in each pair of tables. For each table, graph the ordered pairs formed by each input and output and draw a ray through the points. Then compare the graphs.

1.

Rule: Subtract 3	
Input	Output
6	?
8	?
?	?
11	?
?	?

Rule: Subtract 6	
Input	Output
6	?
8	?
?	?
11	?
?	?

2.

Rule: Multiply by 2	
Input	Output
0	?
1	?
?	?
?	?
5	?

Rule: Multiply by 4	
Input	Output
0	?
1	?
?	?
?	?
5	?

3.

Rule: Multiply by 2	
Input	Output
?	?
?	?
?	?
?	?
?	?

Rule: Multiply by $\frac{1}{2}$	
Input	Output
?	?
?	?
?	?
?	?
?	?

LEARN

For each problem:

(a) Complete each function table using the same set of input values. For the input values that are missing, choose your own values.

(b) For each table, use the First-Quadrant Grids printout to graph the ordered pairs formed by each input and output. Place both sets of points on one graph. Draw a ray through each of the sets of points.

(c) Compare the graphs in as many ways as you can.

1.

Rule: Subtract 1	
Input	Output
6	?
8	?
?	?
11	?
?	?

Rule: Subtract 6	
Input	Output
6	?
8	?
?	?
11	?
?	?

2.

Rule: Multiply by 3	
Input	Output
?	?
?	?
?	?

Rule: Multiply by $\frac{1}{3}$	
Input	Output
?	?
?	?
?	?

T R Y   I T

3. State the actions and thinking you used during this lesson as a math learner.

Math Thinking and Actions
I made sense of problems by • Explaining to myself what a problem means and what it asks for • Using drawings or diagrams to represent a problem I was solving
I explained my math thinking clearly.
I tried out new ways to check if an answer is reasonable.
Other

TRY IT

Find the Perimeter of Plane Figures

Perimeter of Plane Figures

Worked Examples

You can add side lengths or use a formula to find the perimeter of regular and irregular plane figures.

PROBLEM Workers need to replace the reflective tape around a stop sign. To know how much tape is needed, the workers must find the perimeter of the stop sign. What is the perimeter of the stop sign?

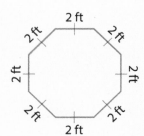

SOLUTION 1 Add the lengths of the sides.

$$2 + 2 + 2 + 2 + 2 + 2 + 2 + 2 = 16$$

SOLUTION 2 Use a formula.

1 Note that all the sides are the same length. You know they are same length because each side has one tick mark.

2 Count the sides. There are 8 sides. The shape is an octagon.

3 Write a formula to multiply the number of sides by the length of the sides.

$$P = 8s$$

The variable *P* stands for the perimeter. The variable *s* stands for the length of 1 side of the octagon.

4 Substitute 2 for *s* into the octagon perimeter formula.

$$P = 8(2)$$
$$P = 16$$

ANSWER The stop sign has a perimeter of 16 feet.

Write a formula for finding the perimeter of the plane figure. Find the perimeter.

1. Mr. Kipp wants to place hexagonal tiles on the ground to make a patio. He needs to know the perimeter of each tile to determine how many tiles he will need for the patio. What is the perimeter of this hexagonal tile?

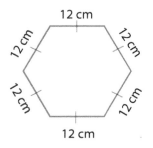

2. Simone wants to put ribbon around a triangular pennant she made for her favorite sports team. The pennant is an equilateral triangle with side lengths of 1.5 meters. What is the perimeter of the pennant?

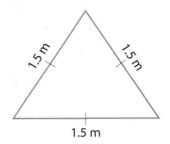

1.5 m
1.5 m
1.5 m

3. A chalk line is needed around home plate on a baseball field. To mark the plate, you need to know the perimeter. What is the perimeter of home plate?

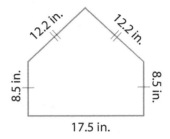

12.2 in.
12.2 in.
8.5 in.
8.5 in.
17.5 in.

4. Putt-Putt Planet miniature golf course has added a new 18th hole and needs to place wooden beams to outline the hole. To determine how much wood is needed, workers must find the perimeter of the 18th hole. What is the perimeter?

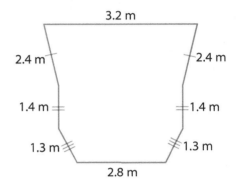

3.2 m
2.4 m
2.4 m
1.4 m
1.4 m
1.3 m
1.3 m
2.8 m

5. Thea plans to use glass square tiles in a mosaic she is building. The length of one side of each tile is 9.4 centimeters. What is the perimeter of each square tile?

6. Scott planted sunflower seeds in a garden shaped like a rectangle. He put a wooden border around the garden. The length of the garden is 8.25 feet. The width of the garden is 3.5 feet. What is the perimeter of the rectangular-shaped garden?

LEARN

Nets, Solids, and Surface Area

Solve Surface Area Problems

Worked Examples

You can find the surface area of a rectangular prism and a cube.

PROBLEM 1 What is the surface area of this rectangular prism? Use the rectangular prism's net and an equation to find the answer.

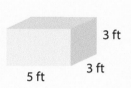

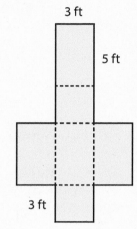

SOLUTION

1. Read the measurement labels on the sides of the rectangular prism's faces. The rectangular prism has a length of 5 feet, a width of 3 feet, and a height of 3 feet.

2. Read and record the measurements of each figure on the net. Write the area of each figure as an expression of length • width. ⟶

3. Use the expressions to write an equation to find the rectangular prism's surface area.

$$\text{surface area} = (3 \cdot 5) + (3 \cdot 5) + (3 \cdot 5) + (3 \cdot 5) + (3 \cdot 3) + (3 \cdot 3)$$
$$= 4(3 \cdot 5) + 2(3 \cdot 3)$$
$$= 4(15) + 2(9)$$
$$= 60 + 18$$
$$= 78$$

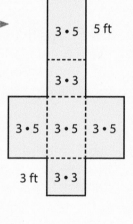

ANSWER The surface area of the rectangular prism is 78 square feet.

L E A R N

PROBLEM 2 What is the surface area of this rectangular prism?
Use the rectangular prism's net and an equation to find the answer.

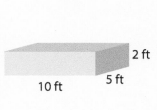

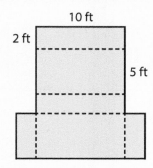

SOLUTION

1 Read the measurement labels on the sides of the rectangular prism's faces.
It has sides that measure 10 feet, 5 feet, and 2 feet. Some rectangular prisms,
such as this one, have sides of three different lengths rather than two different
lengths. That means you'll have three different expressions in your equation.

2 Read and record the measurements
of each figure on the net. Write the
area of each figure as an expression
of length • width. ——————————————→

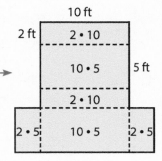

3 Use the expressions to write an equation to find the
rectangular prism's surface area.

surface area $= (10 \cdot 5) + (10 \cdot 5) + (2 \cdot 10) + (2 \cdot 10) + (2 \cdot 5) + (2 \cdot 5)$

$= 2(10 \cdot 5) + 2(2 \cdot 10) + 2(2 \cdot 5)$

$= 2(50) + 2(20) + 2(10)$

$= 100 + 40 + 20$

$= 160$

ANSWER The surface area of the rectangular prism is 160 square feet.

LEARN

Find the surface area. Use the net to help you.

1. rectangular prism

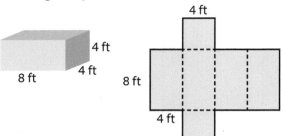

2. rectangular prism

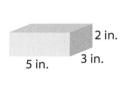 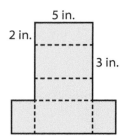

PROBLEM 3 What is the surface area of this cube? Use only an equation.

SOLUTION Multiply the number of congruent faces in a cube (6) by the area of each face. For the area of a face, write length • width.

surface area $= 6(4 • 4)$

$= 6(16)$

$= 96$

4 ft

ANSWER The surface area of the cube is 96 square feet.

Find the surface area. Use an equation.

3. cube

3 cm

4. cube

5 m

Write an equation to solve the problem. Include the unit of measure with the answer.

5. Mr. Sanchez wants to paint a toy box for his granddaughter. The toy box is a cube shape. Mr. Sanchez needs to know the surface area of the toy box so he can buy the correct amount of paint. What is the surface area of the toy box?

2 ft

6. Rachel wants to wrap several boxes that are rectangular prisms. She needs to find the surface area of one box to help her know how much wrapping paper to buy. What is the surface area of one box?

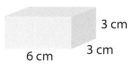

3 cm

6 cm   3 cm

Nets, Solids, and Surface Area

Find Surface Area

Find the surface area of the cube.

1. 7 mm

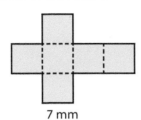

7 mm

2. 3 cm

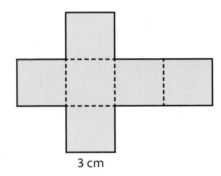

3 cm

3.

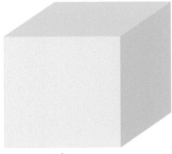

4 ft

Find the surface area of the rectangular prism.

4.

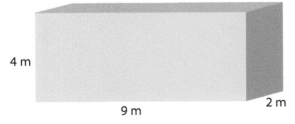

4 m

9 m

2 m

What is the surface area of the figure? Choose the answer.

5.

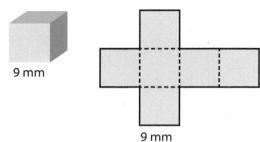

9 mm

9 mm

A. 54 mm² B. 81 mm² C. 486 mm² D. 729 mm²

6.

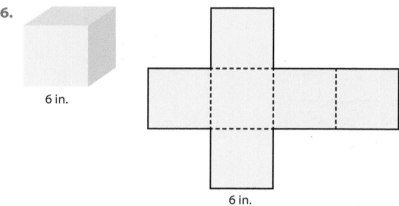

6 in.

6 in.

A. 36 in² B. 144 in² C. 216 in² D. 288 in²

7.

2 cm
5 cm 3 cm

A. 20 cm² B. 30 cm² C. 50 cm² D. 62 cm²

8.

2 cm
10 cm 6 cm

A. 184 cm² B. 120 cm² C. 50 cm² D. 24 cm²

TRY IT

Area of Irregular Shapes

Solve Area Problems

Worked Examples

You can estimate the area of an irregular shape.

PROBLEM What is the approximate area of this lake? Each square represents 1 square mile (1 mi²).

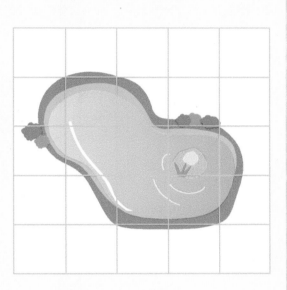

SOLUTION Follow the steps to make your estimate.

1 Look at the lake to see if it is irregular. An irregular shape has some parts that cover parts of squares on a grid. The lake has sections that cover only parts of squares, so it is irregular.

2 Count the whole squares covered by the lake and its border. The lake covers 5 whole squares on the grid.

3 Count the partial squares covered by the lake and its border. The lake covers 11 partial squares on the grid.

4 Combine the partial squares. Estimate how much of a whole square each partial square represents. Think about if each partial square fills about $\frac{1}{4}, \frac{1}{2}$, or $\frac{3}{4}$ of the whole square. Count the whole squares you get. You could estimate that the combined partial squares would equal about 4 whole squares.

5 Add the 5 whole squares you counted to the 4 squares made up of partial squares.

ANSWER A close approximate answer would be 9 square miles. Because this shape is irregular, other approximate answers are acceptable. Approximate answers for this problem can range from 5 square miles to 16 square miles.

LEARN

Solve.

1. Find the approximate area of this rug on a tile floor. Each square represents 1 square foot.

2. Tanya is raking leaves in her yard. Her yard is the irregular green shape on the grid. What is the approximate area of her yard? Each square represents 1 square yard.

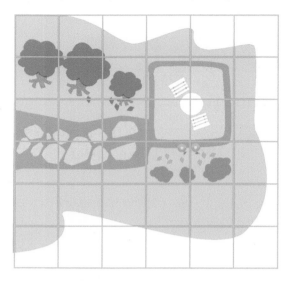

3. What is the approximate area of this swimming pool including the slide, border, and plants? Each square represents 4 square foot.

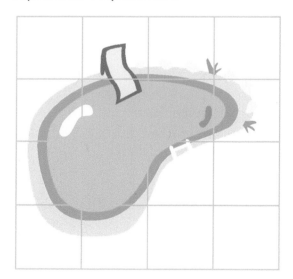

4. This drawing represents the shape of the state of Nevada. What is the approximate area of this shape? Each square represents 10,000 square miles.

Nevada

L E A R N

Area of Irregular Shapes

Area and Irregular Shapes

Solve.

1. What is the approximate area of this garden? Each square represents 1 square foot.

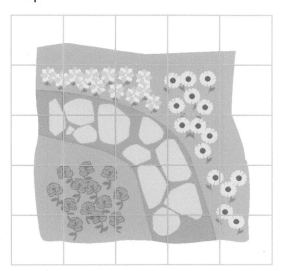

2. What is the approximate area of this pond? Each square represents 1 square yard.

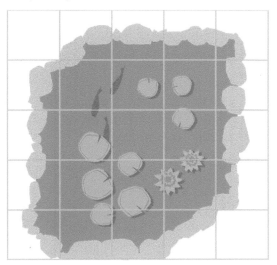

3. What is the approximate area of this backyard? Each square represents 1 square yard.

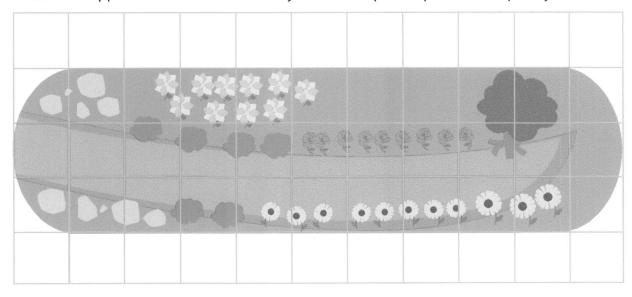

TRY IT

4. What is the approximate area of this lake? Each square represents 1 square kilometer.

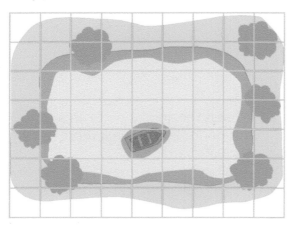

5. What is the approximate area of this tan-colored paint spill? Each square represents 1 square centimeter.

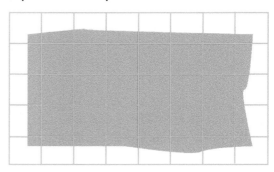

6. What is the approximate area of this kite? Each square represents 1 square centimeter.

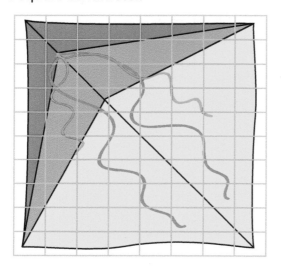

7. What is the approximate area of this campground? Each square represents 1 square meter.

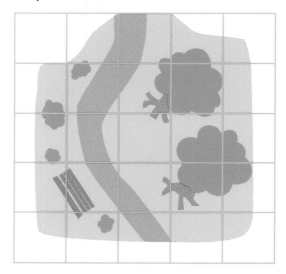

How Many Cubes Does It Take?

Measure Volume

Find the volume.

1.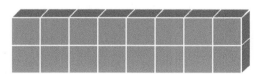

2.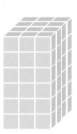

Solve.

3. Jack stacked these cubes.

How many cubes did he use?

4. Look at how Allison stacked her cubes.

How many cubes did she use?

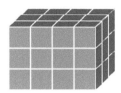

Choose the answer.

5. The picture shows 1 cube.
John used the cubes to build the shape.

How many cubes are in the shape John built?

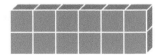

A. 24

B. 20

C. 14

D. 12

T R Y   I T

Choose the answer.

6. The picture shows 1 cube.
Laura built the wall with the cubes.

How many cubes did Laura use to build the wall?

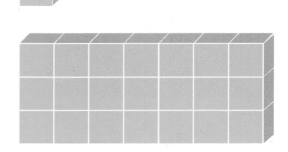

A. 7

B. 14

C. 21

D. 28

7. Marcus is using blocks to make a cube. If each cube is solid and has no holes, how many blocks did Marcus use?

A. 16

B. 48

C. 64

D. 96

8. What is the volume, in cubic centimeters, of the figure shown?

A. 15 cm³

B. 21 cm³

C. 35 cm³

D. 105 cm³

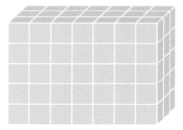

= 1 cm³

9. Matilda is filling a box with 1-inch sugar cubes. She filled the bottom with one layer as shown in the picture.

When she completely fills the box, how many sugar cubes will be in the box?

A. 12

B. 19

C. 84

D. 133

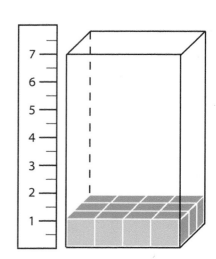

TRY IT

10. About how many cubes were used to make this figure?

A. 45   B. 60

C. 90   D. 120

11. About how many cubes were used to make this figure?

A. 50   B. 30

C. 20   D. 10

12. Which rectangular prism has a volume closest to 100 cubic units?

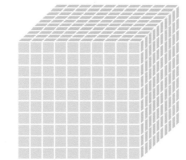

A.

B.

C.

13. Which cube has a volume closest to 30 cubic units?

A.

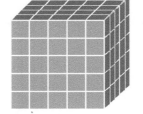

B.

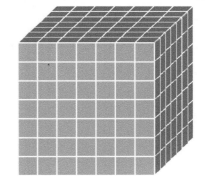

C.

Solve.

14. Debbie is filling a box with 1-inch cubes. She filled the bottom layer as shown.

Debbie wants to completely fill the box. Including the cubes she has already put in the box, how many cubes will Debbie use in all?

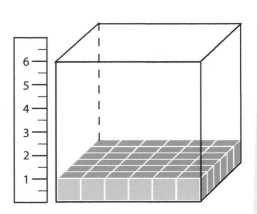

T R Y I T

Volume of Solid Figures (A)

Practice Volume of Solid Figures

Read the problem and follow the directions.

1. There are 15 centimeter cubes in each layer in this rectangular prism. Explain why the volume of this rectangular prism is 90 cubic centimeters.

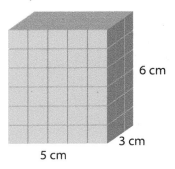

6 cm

3 cm

5 cm

2. Find the volume of the rectangular prisms by counting the cubes in each layer.

Each cube is 1 cm³.

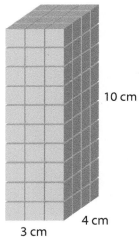

10 cm

4 cm

3 cm

TRY IT

Choose the answer.

3.   Each cube is 1 cm³.

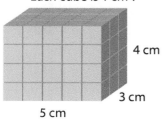

4 cm

3 cm

5 cm

A. 12 cm³   B. 15 cm³

C. 60 cm³   D. 94 cm³

4.   Each cube is 1 in³.

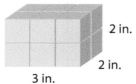

2 in.

2 in.

3 in.

A. 7 in³   B. 12 in³

C. 24 in³   D. 322 in³

5.   Each cube is 1 in³.

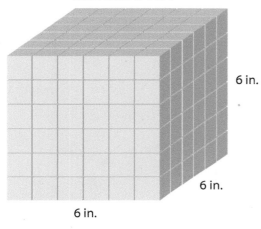

6 in.

6 in.

6 in.

A. 12 in³   B. 36 cm³

C. 72 cm³   D. 216 in³

6.   Each cube is 1 in³.

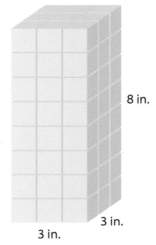

8 in.

3 in.

3 in.

A. 14 in³   B. 72 in³

C. 216 in³   D. 338 in³

T R Y   I T

Volume of Solid Figures (B)

Use the Volume Formula

You can use the volume formula $V = lwh$ to find the volume of a rectangular prism. You can also use the volume formula to find the length, width, or height of a rectangular prism if you know the area and two of the other measurements.

PROBLEM 1 What is the volume of the cereal box?

SOLUTION Substitute the given values into the volume formula $V = lwh$.

$V = lwh$
$V = 7 \cdot 3 \cdot 10$
$V = 210$

Cereal

height 10 in.

12.5 ounces.

width 3 in.

length 7 in.

ANSWER The volume of the cereal box is 210 cubic inches.

PROBLEM 2 The volume of this storage container is 1,400 cubic inches. The length is 14 inches and the width is 20 inches. What is the measure of the height of the storage container?

height ? in.

width 20 in.

length 14 in.

SOLUTION Substitute the given values into the volume formula $V = Bh$. Solve for the missing value.

$V = Bh$
$1{,}400 = (14 \cdot 20) \cdot h$
$1{,}400 = 280 \cdot h$
$1{,}400 \div 280 = 280 \div 280 \cdot h$
$1{,}400 \div 280 = h$
$5 = h$

ANSWER The height of the storage container is 5 inches.

Use the volume formula $V = lwh$, or $V = Bh$, to solve.

1. Find the volume of this rectangular prism.

   The length is 7 inches.
   The width is 9 inches.
   The height is 4 inches.

   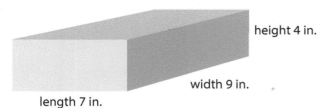

   height 4 in.
   width 9 in.
   length 7 in.

2. What is the volume of this rectangular prism?

   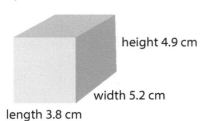

   height 4.9 cm
   width 5.2 cm
   length 3.8 cm

3. What is the length of this rectangular prism?

   volume = 252 ft³

   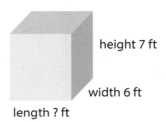

   height 7 ft
   width 6 ft
   length ? ft

4. What is the volume of this cube?

   Hint: A cube is a special kind of rectangular prism.

   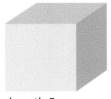

   length 5 m

5. What is the height of this rectangular prism?

   volume = 24 cm³

   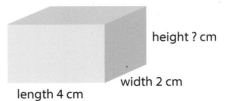

   height ? cm
   width 2 cm
   length 4 cm

LEARN

Use the volume formula $V = lwh$, or $V = Bh$, to solve.

6. What is the volume of a shipping box with length 6 feet, width 12 feet, and height 13 feet?

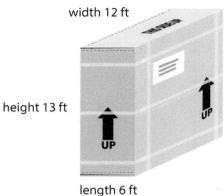

width 12 ft

height 13 ft

UP

UP

length 6 ft

7. What is the volume of a toy chest with length 3.6 feet, width 2.1 feet, and height 2.4 feet?

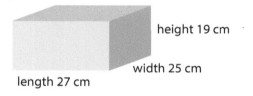

width 2.1 ft

height 2.4 ft

length 3.6 ft

8. What is the width of this rectangular prism?

volume = 72 m³

height 2 m

length 6 m

width ? m

9. What is the volume of this rectangular prism?

height 19 cm

width 25 cm

length 27 cm

10. What is the volume of this cube-shaped gift box?

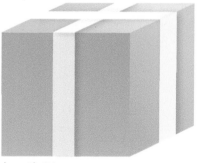

length 8 in.

LEARN

Volume of Solid Figures (B)

Practice the Formula for Volume

Use the volume formula $V = lwh$, or $V = Bh$, to solve.

1. Explain how to calculate the volume of this shoe box. What is the volume of the shoe box?

height 6 in.

width 8 in.

length 12 in.

2. What is the volume of this rectangular prism?

Each cube is 1 cm³.

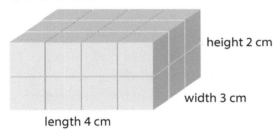

height 2 cm

width 3 cm

length 4 cm

3. The volume of a computer box is 1,904 cubic inches. The length is 17 inches and the height is 16 inches. What is the measure of the width of the box?

TRY IT

Steps to Solve Story Problems (B)

Analyze Problems and Make Steps

Worked Examples

You can select the information you need to solve a story problem. You can figure out what steps to use for solving the problem and put the steps in order.

PROBLEM Camille was studying the art of American painter Jackson Pollock. For an art lesson, she needed to write a report and paint a picture in the painter's style. She and her mother decided to go to the art supply store. Camille wrote a list that included paintbrushes, at least 4 different colors of paint, 2 sheets of poster board, and construction paper.

At the store, Camille selected the supplies. When she had finished, she and her mother were ready to purchase the following items:

- 1 package of paintbrushes: $4.99
- 2 large bottles of paint, red and blue: 3 bottles for $5.79
- 2 small bottles of paint, orange and green: $1.39 each
- 2 sheets of poster board: $2.29 each
- 1 package of white construction paper: $2.79

Camille and her mother decided that Camille will pay for the paint and the 2 sheets of poster board. Her mother will pay for the other items.

What steps would you follow to calculate how much Camille will pay?

SOLUTION

UNDERSTAND THE PROBLEM

Ask yourself the following questions to help you understand what the problem is asking:

- Do I understand all the words in the problem? If you don't, then look them up in a dictionary or ask someone who is likely to know the meaning of the word.

- What am I asked to find, explain, or show? You need to find the amount that Camille will pay.

- How can I restate the problem in my own words? An example is this question: How much money will Camille owe for 4 bottles of paint and 2 sheets of poster board?

- Can I sketch something to help me understand the problem? There isn't an obvious sketch that can be used to solve this problem. But in other problems, a sketch might help you.

- What information do I have, what do I need, and what do I **not** need? You have some information about the cost of various art supplies to be purchased. You need more information about prices, such as the per-item price for the large bottles of paint. You don't need the cost of the paintbrushes and construction paper or the color of the paint.

DEVISE A PLAN

You can follow a set of steps to help you find the amount Camille will pay. A list of the steps in order can help you.

1 Figure out the cost of the 2 large paint bottles.

2 Figure out the cost of the 2 small paint bottles.

3 Figure out the cost of the 2 sheets of poster board.

4 Add those three amounts to get the total amount that Camille will pay.

CARRY OUT THE PLAN

Go through your list to help you stay organized.

Do Steps 1, 2, and 3 in any order. Use your reasoning skills to figure out which steps you need to do in a specific order.

1 Find the cost of the 2 large paint bottles.

- Divide the cost of 3 bottles by 3. $5.79 \div 3$

- Multiply the quotient by 2. $1.93 \cdot 2$

2 Find the cost of the 2 small paint bottles.

$1.39 \cdot 2$

3 Find the cost of the 2 sheets of poster board.

$2.29 \cdot 2$

4 Add the costs of the supplies.
The 2 large paint bottles cost $3.86.
The 2 small paint bottles cost $2.78.
The 2 sheets of poster board cost $4.58.
$3.86 + $2.78 + $4.58

LOOK BACK

Ask yourself these questions:

- Did I answer the question of how much money Camille will pay for the art supplies? Yes, the answer is the cost of her share of the supplies.

- How should I decide if the answer makes sense? Round the prices of the items and use estimation to get an estimated answer. Then compare it with the actual answer. At each step, you can round the prices to the nearest dollar and then multiply. Then add the products.

- Have I forgotten anything? Look back at the problem to make sure you haven't forgotten anything. Double-check the math.

ANSWER

1 Figure out the cost of the 2 large paint bottles.

2 Figure out the cost of the 2 small paint bottles.

3 Figure out the cost of the 2 sheets of poster board.

4 Add those three amounts to get the total amount that Camille will pay.

L E A R N

Read the problem and follow the directions.

1. Answer the question about the following story problem:

   Gerard and Emily rode their bikes on a bike trail. Gerard rode for 2 hours at an average speed of 8 miles per hour. Emily rode for 3 hours at an average speed of 6 miles per hour.

   What steps would you follow to calculate the difference in the distances they rode?

2. Answer the question about the following story problem:

   Clarice had 18 containers that she needed to fill with water and carry outside. She could fill and carry 3 containers every 5 minutes. How many containers would she still need to fill after 15 minutes had passed?

   What step should you do first to solve this story problem?

3. List steps in a correct order for solving the story problem. Then solve the problem.

   Don wants to earn money so he can save to go on a trip. He offers these services to his 7 neighbors:

   - dog walking: $2.50 per dog
   - car washing: $4.00 per car
   - driveway sweeping: $1.25 per driveway
   - watering and weed pulling: $9.50 per week for each flower bed or vegetable bed

   A neighbor with 2 driveways asks him to sweep both of his driveways. A neighbor with 3 dogs asks him to walk 2 of the dogs. A neighbor with 4 cars asks him to wash 3 of the cars. A neighbor with a flower bed asks him to weed the bed for 2 weeks.

   What steps would you follow to calculate how much Don earned from these jobs?

LEARN

Break Down Multistep Problems

Simpler Parts

Worked Examples

You can determine when and how to break a story problem into simpler parts.

PROBLEM Answer the questions about this story problem:

- Eduardo saved $3.00 from his allowance every week for 12 weeks. He spent $\frac{3}{4}$ of the saved amount on a baseball glove. Later, he spent $\frac{1}{3}$ of the remaining amount on a baseball book. How much money does he have left?

Should the problem be broken into simpler problems? If so, how should it be done?

SOLUTION

UNDERSTAND THE PROBLEM
To figure out if the problem should be broken into simpler parts, ask yourself these questions:

- What am I asked to find, explain, or show? You are asked to find how much of Eduardo's savings of 12 weeks he has left.
- How can I restate the problem in my own words? Eduardo saved a sum of money. He spent a fraction of the money. Then later he spent another fraction of the remaining money.
- What information do I have, what do I need, and what do I **not** need? You know how much he saved each week for 12 weeks. You know the fractional amounts he spent on a baseball glove and a book. You know he spent the money at different times. You need to calculate how much he saved, each amount he spent, and how much he has left.

Yes, the problem requires several calculations, so it should be broken into simpler parts. To break it into simpler problems, devise a plan.

DEVISE A PLAN
To break the problem into simpler parts, make a list of the calculations you need to do.

1. Calculate how much Eduardo saved in 12 weeks.
2. Calculate how much he spent on the baseball glove.
3. Subtract that amount from his savings.
4. Calculate how much of his remaining savings he spent on the baseball book.
5. Subtract that amount from his remaining savings.

LEARN

CARRY OUT THE PLAN

1 Multiply to find out how much Eduardo saved in 12 weeks.

2 Multiply the amount of money he saved by $\frac{3}{4}$ to find out how much he spent on the glove.

3 Subtract that amount from his savings.

4 Multiply the difference by $\frac{1}{3}$ to find out how much he spent on the book.

5 Subtract that amount from his remaining savings.

LOOK BACK

Ask yourself these questions:

- Did I answer the question of whether to break the problem into simpler parts? Yes.

- Did I answer the question of how to break the problem into simpler parts? Yes. You made a list of the calculations needed for solving the problem.

ANSWER Yes, the problem should be broken into simpler parts. The simpler parts are the calculations needed to find the final answer.

Read the problem and follow the directions.

1. What calculations could be used to solve this problem?

   A popular singer was on a concert tour. Attendance at the concerts was 7,845 for each of the first 4 performances and 6,920 for the final performance. How many people in all attended the concerts?

Choose the answer.

2. Which describes the calculations that could be used to solve this problem?

   A coin collector keeps 1,482 coins in 6 jars. Each jar contains an equal number of coins. Nine coins in each jar are gold coins. How many coins in each jar are **not** gold coins?

   A. Subtract 6 from 1,482. Then divide by 9.

   B. Add 6 to 1,482. Then divide by 9.

   C. Divide 1,482 by 6. Then subtract 9.

   D. Multiply 1,482 by 6. Then subtract 9.

3. Read the problem and review the data in the table. What calculations could be used to solve the following problem?

What is the cost of 8 packages of stickers?

A. Multiply $3.45 by 8.
   Subtract $2.29 from the product.

B. Multiply $3.45 by 8.
   Add $2.75 to the product.

C. Divide $5.99 by 8.

D. Multiply $3.45 by 8.

Scrapbooking Supplies	
scrapbooks	$5.99 each
stickers	$3.45 per package
rubber stamps	$2.29 each
stencils	$2.75 each

4. Which simpler problems could be calculated to solve this problem?

Ray, Nancy, and Elaine collected a total of 982 cans of food for the canned food drive. Ray collected 178 cans. Nancy and Elaine collected an equal number of cans. How many cans did Nancy collect?

A. Find the number of cans Ray collected.
   Then find the total number of cans Ray, Nancy, and Elaine collected.

B. Find the total number of cans Ray, Nancy, and Elaine collected.
   Then find the number of cans Nancy collected.

C. Find the number of cans Nancy collected.
   Then find the total number of cans Nancy and Elaine collected.

D. Find the number of cans Nancy and Elaine collected.
   Then find the number of cans Nancy collected.

LEARN

Choose the problem-solving strategy and explanation that correctly show how to solve the problem.

1. Daniella made 1 triangle with 3 toothpicks. She discovered she could make 2 triangles if she used 5 toothpicks. If she used 7 toothpicks, she could make 3 triangles. How many toothpicks would Daniella need to make 7 triangles?

   A. **Write an equation.**
   $(1 \cdot 3) + (2 \cdot 5) + (3 \cdot 7) = ?$
   Calculate the number of toothpicks needed to make each triangle and add them all up.

   B. **Guess and test.**
   Guess 17 toothpicks for 7 triangles. Test your guess by drawing the toothpick triangles. If you couldn't draw 7 triangles, revise your guess. Test your guess again. Keep trying.

   C. **Draw a diagram.**
   Draw a diagram of 3 triangles using 7 lines to represent toothpicks. Keep adding lines until you have 7 triangles. Count the number of lines.

2. The perimeter of 1 face of a cube is 28 cm. What is the surface area of the cube?

   A. **Write equations.**
   Calculate the length of 1 edge of the cube. Let n represent the length.
   $28 = 4n$
   The length of 1 edge of the cube is 7 cm.
   Calculate the area of 1 face. $A = 7 \cdot 7$
   Calculate the surface area of the cube. $S = 49 \cdot 6$

   B. **Guess and test.**
   Guess that the surface area of 1 face is 60 cm². Calculate that the area of 1 face is 10 cm². Calculate that the perimeter of 1 face is 40 cm. That guess didn't work, so make another guess. Guess that the surface area of 1 face is 42 cm². Calculate that the area of 1 face is 7 cm². So the perimeter of 1 face is 28 cm.

   C. **Work backward.**
   The perimeter of 1 face is 28 cm. So the length of 1 face is 14 cm. The area of 1 face would be $14 \cdot 14$. Then multiply that answer by 6 to calculate the surface area.

TRY IT

3. Kent is planting rows of seeds in the community garden. He plants 5 seeds in his first row, 11 seeds in his second row, and 17 seeds in his third row. If Kent uses the same pattern, how many seeds will he plant in his 7th row?

   A. **Write an equation.**
   $(1 \cdot 5) + (2 \cdot 11) + (3 \cdot 17) = ?$
   Calculate the number of seeds needed in each row and add them together.

   B. **Draw a diagram.**
   Draw 1 seed next to 5 seeds, then 2 seeds next to 11 seeds, and 3 seeds next to 17 seeds. Keep drawing and count all the seeds.

   C. **Make a table.**
   Write the seed-row numbers 1, 2, 3, 4, 5, 6, 7 as column names at the top of the table. In the first row of the table, write 5 in column 1, 11 in column 2, and 17 in column 3. Look for the pattern. Fill in the rest of the table using the same pattern.

4. Denzel can paint 12 tiles in an hour. How many tiles can Denzel paint in $4\frac{1}{2}$ hours?

   A. **Make a table.**
   Look for a pattern in your table.

Hours	1	2	3	4	5	6
Tiles	4.5	4.5	4.5	4.5	4.5	4.5

   B. **Write an equation.**
   Let n equal the number of tiles Denzel can paint in $4\frac{1}{2}$ hours.
   $n = 12 \cdot 4\frac{1}{2} = 12 \cdot \frac{9}{2} = \frac{108}{2} = 54$
   Denzel can paint 54 tiles in $4\frac{1}{2}$ hours.

   C. **Use simpler numbers.**
   Suppose that Denzel could paint only 10 tiles per hour. Calculate how many tiles he could paint in 4 hours: $10 \cdot 4 = 40$. So in 4 hours, he can paint 40 tiles. Now that you have figured out how to solve the problem, go back and solve it using fractions.

TRY IT

Choose the problem-solving strategy and explanation that correctly show how to solve the problem.

5. Maddie bought 3 more pounds of flour than Kath. Together Kath and Maddie bought 13 pounds of flour. How many pounds of flour did Kath buy?

    A. **Guess and test.**
        Guess that Kath bought 2 pounds of flour. This means that Maddie would have bought 5 pounds, because $2 + 3 = 5$. Add $2 + 5$. If the sum doesn't equal 13, revise your guess to be that Kath bought 3 pounds of flour. Figure out how many pounds of flour Maddie bought. Is this sum equal to 13? If not, revise your guess, and test your answer again.

    B. **Draw a diagram.**
        Draw 13 circles to represent the 13 pounds of flour. Divide the circles into two equal groups. Then multiply one group by 3.

    C. **Write an equation.**
        Let m represent the number pounds of flour Kath bought.
        $(3 \cdot m) + 2 = 13$

6. Derek earned some money over the summer. He charged $7 to wash a car and $4 to walk a dog. He washed 12 cars and walked 6 dogs in August. How much money did Derek make in August?

    A. **Work backward.**
        Derek washed 12 cars, so count backward from 12 to 7 to figure out how much money he made washing cars. He walked 6 dogs, so count back from 6 to 4 to see how much money he made walking dogs. Add the two amounts together.

    B. **Write equations.**
        Multiply the number of cars washed by the amount charged per car.
        $12 \cdot 7 = 84$
        Then multiply the number of dogs walked by the amount charged per dog. $6 \cdot 4 = 24$
        Add the two products together to find the total amount earned.

    C. **Draw a picture.**
        Draw 12 cars and 6 dogs. Count the cars and dogs.

TRY IT

7. The animal park has 63 butterflies in a special environment for butterflies. There are 28 red butterflies, 19 white butterflies, and the rest are yellow. How many butterflies are yellow?

   A. **Write an equation.**
      $63 - 28 - 19 = ?$

   B. **Guess and test.**
      Guess that there are 20 yellow butterflies. Add 20 to the number of red and white butterflies. Is your answer 28? If not, revise your guess, and test your answer again.

   C. **Draw a diagram.**
      Draw 19 dots. Then figure out how many dots you need to get to 28 butterflies in all.

8. Charlotte was selling pies at a bake sale. She sold 13 pies before lunch and another 5 after lunch. At the end of the day, Charlotte had 8 pies left. How many pies did Charlotte start the day with?

   A. **Write an equation.**
      $8 + 5 - 13 = ?$

   B. **Draw a picture.**
      Draw 8 circles. Add 5 circles and then add 13 circles.

   C. **Guess and test.**
      Guess that Charlotte started with 20 pies. Subtract 8. Is your answer 13? If not, revise your guess, and test your answer again.

TRY IT

Mathematical Reasoning Methods (B)

Practice Solving Nonroutine Problems

Choose the problem-solving strategy and explanation that correctly show how to solve the problem.

1. Artie was saving pennies. On the first day, he saved 2 pennies. The next day, he saved twice as many, giving him a total of 6 pennies $(2 + 4)$. He continued doubling the number of pennies he saved for 10 days. How many pennies did Artie have by the end of the 10th day?

   A. **Write an equation.**
   $10 \cdot (2 + 4) = b$
   Add the pennies he saved on the first and second days. Then multiply by the total number of days.

   B. **Make a table.**
   In the Day 1 column, write 2 pennies.
   In the Day 2 column, write 4 pennies.
   In the Day 3 column, write 8 pennies.
   Continue that pattern through Day 10. The solution is the sum of the numbers of pennies from each day.

   C. **Draw a diagram.**
   Draw 2 pennies and label them Day 1. Draw 6 pennies and label them Day 2. Draw 14 pennies and label them Day 3. Continue this pattern for the 10 days and then count all the pennies.

2. The temperature was 20°F at noon. The temperature increased 3°F per hour until 8:00 p.m. What was the temperature at 6:00 p.m.?

   A. **Guess and test.**
   Guess that the temperature will be 30°F. Find the difference between 20°F and 30°F and divide that by 3. If the answer is less than 6 (the number of hours between noon and 6:00 p.m.), revise your guess, and test your answer again.

   B. **Make a table.**
   Write noon, 1:00 p.m., 2:00 p.m., 3:00 p.m., 4:00 p.m., 5:00 p.m., and 6:00 p.m. on the top row. Write the temperature starting at 20°F under noon in the second row. Write the temperatures, increasing by 3°F, in the remaining boxes on the second row. The correct answer is the temperature at 6:00 p.m.

   C. **Work backward.**
   Start with 6:00 p.m. Subtract 6 hours from 6:00 p.m. to get to noon. Then multiply 20°F by 6 to find out the temperature at 6:00 p.m.

TRY IT

3. The surface area of a cube is 24 square inches. What is the perimeter of a face of the cube?

A. **Guess and test.**
Guess that the perimeter of a face is 20 inches, So each side of a face is 5 inches. The area of each face would then be 25 square inches. Double that number to get the surface area. The product is greater than 24 square inches. Guess another number, and test it.

B. **Write equations.**
Calculate the surface area of a face of the cube.
Let a represent the area of each face of the cube.
$24 = 6a$, so $4 = a$
Calculate the length of each side. Let s represent the length of each side of each face of the cube.
$s \cdot s = 4$, so $s = 2$
Calculate the perimeter of each face.
$P = 4 \cdot 2$

C. **Work backward.**
Start with the surface area of 24. Divide by 4 to figure out the area of each face. Then multiply that answer by 4 to get the perimeter.

4. Julie wants to make a rectangular playground that has an area of 160 square feet. She wants to put a rope fence around it, but she wants to use as little rope as possible. What are the dimensions Julie should use for her playground?

A. **Use objects to model the problem.**
Arrange 160 square tiles in different patterns until you get a rectangular shape. Count the number of tiles on the perimeter of this shape.

B. **Write an equation.**
Write an equation that could be used to calculate the area of a rectangle. Use guess and check to find two numbers that when multiplied will give a product of 160.

C. **Look for a pattern.**
Make a list of all possible combinations of length and width that would equal an area of 160 square feet. Then start calculating the perimeter of each rectangle. Look for a pattern to decrease the number of calculations you have to make.

TRY IT

Choose the series of steps that will result in the correct answer.

5. Timmy bought twice as many plums as apples. He bought 4 more plums than bananas. He bought 6 apples. How many bananas did Timmy buy?

   A. Start with 6. Multiply 6 by 2. Then subtract 4.

   B. Start with 6. Multiply 6 by 2. Then add 4.

   C. Start with 4. Add 4 and 6. Then multiply the sum by 2 and add 4.

6. A number is multiplied by 2. Then 8 is added to the product. The sum is then divided by 5. The answer is 8. What was the original number?

   A. Start with 8. Multiply 8 by 5. Then add 8 and multiply the sum by 2.

   B. Start with 8. Add 8 and 5. Then subtract 8 and multiply the sum by 2.

   C. Start with 8. Multiply 8 by 5. Then subtract 8 and divide the difference by 2.

TRY IT

Choose and Use Strategies (A)

Use Tables to Solve Problems

Worked Examples

You can make a table as a strategy to find the solution to some story problems.

PROBLEM   Nyree is 30 years old. Her daughter, Mia, is 6 years old. In how many years will Nyree be twice as old as Mia?

SOLUTION

UNDERSTAND THE PROBLEM
You know Nyree's age and Mia's age now. You need to compare their ages in future years.

DEVISE A PLAN
Use the make-a-table strategy. Put what you know in the table. Create a row for Nyree and a row for Mia. Put their ages now in the first column. To save time and space, have each new column stand for 2 years instead of 1 year.

CARRY OUT THE PLAN

Nyree's age	30	32	34	36	38	40	42	44	46	48
Mia's age	6	8	10	12	14	16	18	20	22	24

As you put ages in each column, check to see if Nyree's age is twice that of Mia. When you get to the column where that happens, stop and count the columns to the right of their current ages. Count each column as 2 years.

LOOK BACK
Look at the table and make sure you wrote the ages and counted the years correctly. Remember that each column of this table stands for 2 years.

ANSWER   Nyree will be twice as old as her daughter in 18 years, when Nyree will be 48 years old and Mia will be 24 years old.

LEARN

Solve by making a table.

1. The temperature at 9:00 p.m. was 28°F. The temperature dropped 3°F each hour until 1:00 a.m. What was the temperature at 1:00 a.m.?

2. Cynthia bought 2 train tickets and a newspaper each day on the way to work. Each newspaper cost $2.50, and each train ticket cost $3.75. How much money did Cynthia spend in 10 days?

3. Ilene needs 2 cups of walnuts and 3 cups of almonds in her snack mix recipe. How many cups of nuts does she need to make 7 batches of snack mix?

4. Some soccer teams from a town are traveling to a tournament. Each team can have 3 coaches and 16 players. There are 12 coaches going to the tournament. How many players are going to the tournament?

Choose and Use Strategies (A)

Practice Using Tables

Memory Jogger

MAKE-A-TABLE STRATEGY

Mrs. Fry uses 4 balls of white yarn and 5 balls of blue yarn to knit a blanket. How many balls of yarn does she need to make 5 blankets?

Number of blankets	1	2	3	4	5
Number of balls of yarn	9	18	27	36	45

Mrs. Fry uses 9 balls of yarn to knit a blanket.

To knit 5 blankets, she will use 45 balls of yarn.

Solve by making a table.

1. Peter is 35 years old. His son Nathan is 10 years old. How many years ago was Peter 6 times older than Nathan?

2. The temperature was 15° at noon. It increased 4°F per hour until 8:00 p.m. What was the temperature at 6:00 p.m.?

3. Tom bought a daisy and 2 roses for each of his 6 cousins. Daisies cost $1.25 each. Roses cost $2.99 each. How much money did Tom spend?

4. Charlie's bread recipe uses 1 cup of whole-wheat flour and 2 cups of white flour for each loaf. How many cups of flour does Charlie need to make 5 loaves of bread?

5. Toby is making a tile mosaic. He puts 3 blue tiles in the first row, 7 blue tiles in the second row, and 11 blue tiles in the third row. If Toby continues using the same pattern, how many blue tiles will he use in the 6th row?

6. Karly can make 1 square with 4 toothpicks. She can make 2 squares with 7 toothpicks. She can make 3 squares with 10 toothpicks. Karly continued making squares to the right of the toothpick squares shown.

When Karly had made 9 squares in all, how many toothpicks had she used?

T R Y I T

Choose and Use Strategies (B)

Write-an-Equation Strategy

Worked Examples

You can solve a problem by writing an equation.

PROBLEM Use an equation to find the sum of the consecutive even numbers 2, 4, 6, 8, 10, and 12.

SOLUTION

UNDERSTAND THE PROBLEM

If you don't understand a word in the problem, look it up in a dictionary. The word *consecutive* means "following in order one after another."

If you were to restate this problem in your own words, you might say this: Use an equation to find the sum of the even whole numbers from 2 through 12.

DEVISE A PLAN

Use an equation to solve the problem.

Background information on an equation to find the sum of consecutive numbers: Carl Friedrich Gauss was a mathematician and astronomer whose research, observations, and conclusions are important in the study of math. He was born in Germany in 1777. When he was a young boy, he came up with an equation to find the sum of consecutive numbers.

In his equation, the variable S stands for the sum. The variable n stands for how many numbers are in the group of consecutive numbers in the problem to be solved.

$$S = \frac{n(n + 1)}{2}$$

Look at Carl Friedrich Gauss's equation. Ask yourself: Would a similar equation work for adding consecutive **even** numbers quickly?

CARRY OUT THE PLAN

1 Compare a list of all consecutive whole numbers 1 through 12 with a list of consecutive even whole numbers 2 through 12:

- consecutive even and odd numbers 1 through 12:
  1, 2, 3, 4, 5, 6, 7, 8, 9, 10, 11, 12
- consecutive even numbers 2 through 12:
  2, 4, 6, 8, 10, 12

2 Look for a pattern in the ordered list of numbers.

- In the consecutive **even and odd** numbers, the third number is 3. In the consecutive **even** numbers, the third number is 6. The number 3 is half of 6.

- In the consecutive **even and odd** numbers, the fifth number is 5. In the consecutive **even** numbers, the fifth number is 10. The number 5 is half of 10.

- If you were to keep checking, you would see that every consecutive even number is twice its corresponding number in the ordered list of consecutive even and odd numbers. So the sums of the even numbers add up more quickly. In fact, they double.

3 Use what you have learned to write an equation to find the sum of consecutive even numbers.

- The following equation results in the sum of consecutive even and odd numbers when S stands for the sum and n stands for how many numbers you are finding the sum of:

$$S = \frac{n(n+1)}{2}$$

- The sum of the consecutive even numbers will be 2 times greater than the sum of the consecutive even and odd numbers. So if you want the right side of the equation to represent twice its current value, you multiply that side by 2, which leaves 1 in the denominator of the fraction. The following equation now shows how to find the sum of consecutive **even** numbers:

$$S = n(n+1)$$

4 You are trying to find the sum of the first 6 even numbers, so $n = 6$. Substitute 6 for n.

$$S = n(n+1)$$
$$S = 6(6+1)$$
$$S = 6(7)$$
$$S = 42$$

Using the equation, find that the sum of the first 6 consecutive even numbers, 2, 4, 6, 8, 10, and 12, is 42.

LEARN

LOOK BACK

Another way to calculate the answer is to add the even numbers without using an equation. Check your math by using an addition shortcut.

Draw arcs to number pairs that add to 14.

$$2 + 12 = 14 \qquad 4 + 10 = 14 \qquad 6 + 8 = 14$$

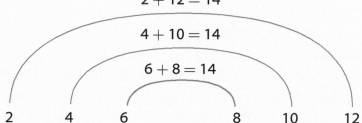

Then add how many sums of 14 there are altogether.

$$14 + 14 + 14 = 42$$

Using an addition shortcut, you find that the sum of the first 6 consecutive even numbers, 2, 4, 6, 8, 10, and 12, is 42.

ANSWER The sum of 2, 4, 6, 8, 10, and 12 is 42.

Use this equation for finding the sum of consecutive even numbers to solve the problem.

$$S = n(n + 1)$$

1. What is the sum of the consecutive even numbers 1 through 16?

2. What is the sum of the consecutive even numbers 1 through 30?

3. What is the sum of the consecutive even numbers 1 through 50?

4. What is the sum of the consecutive even numbers 1 through 62?

Choose and Use Strategies (B)

Guess-and-Test Strategy

Worked Examples

You can guess numbers and test them to find answers to some story problems.

PROBLEM   Mrs. Jensen has collected comic books for 10 years. Her daughter, Sara, just started a comic book collection. Mrs. Jensen has 24 times as many comic books as Sara has. Together, they have 225 comic books. How many comic books does each person have?

SOLUTION

UNDERSTAND THE PROBLEM
If you were to restate the problem in your own words, you might say this: The number of Sara's comic books multiplied by 24 equals the number of comic books Mrs. Jensen has. Together, they have 225 comic books. Find how many comic books each person has.

DEVISE A PLAN
This problem can be solved by the guess-and-test strategy. To make it easier to find the answer, you can combine the strategy with the write-an-equation strategy and the make-a-table strategy. You can use a table by putting your guesses into it.

CARRY OUT THE PLAN

1 Decide the variables that you'll use in the equations.
Represent Mrs. Jensen's comic books with the variable m.
Represent Sara's comic books with the variable d.

2 Translate this sentence into an equation: Mrs. Jensen has 24 times as many comic books as Sara has.
$d \cdot 24 = m$

3 Translate this sentence into an equation: Together, they have 225 comic books.
$m + d = 225$

L E A R N

④ Since you know that Sara has many fewer comic books than Mrs. Jensen has, start by guessing a low number, such as 20, for Sara's number of comic books. Keep guessing. Multiply each guess by 24.

- first guess: $20 \cdot 24 = 480$; That's too high. You don't need to add the two numbers because you already know the second number is too high.
- second guess: $10 \cdot 24 = 240$; That's still too high.
- third guess: $5 \cdot 24 = 120$; Now you need to add 5 to 120 to show adding Sara's number of books to Mrs. Jensen's number of books. You get only 125 instead of 225. That's too low.
- fourth guess: $9 \cdot 24 = 216$; $9 + 216 = 225$

You can keep track of your guesses in a table, such as the following one. When the product of the guessed number and 24 is more than 225, calculating the total is not needed.

First number	Second number	Total	Total too high, too low, or correct?
20	480	not needed	too high
10	240	not needed	too high
5	120	125	too low
9	216	225	correct

LOOK BACK

Check the math. Mrs. Jensen's 216 comic books and Sara's 9 comic books add up to 225. Mrs. Jensen's number of books is 24 times Sara's number.

ANSWER Mrs. Jensen has 216 comic books. Sara has 9 comic books.

Solve. Use the guess-and-test strategy combined with any other strategies you want to use. Use a table to show your work.

1. Joe started a coin collection by buying some coins. His father's coin collection contains 6 times as many coins as Joe has. The total number of coins they own is 49. How many coins does each person have?

2. Tom traveled 175 times as many miles to visit his grandmother as he traveled to visit his uncle. He traveled 2,816 miles in all. How many miles did Tom travel to visit each of his relatives?

Choose and Use Strategies (B)

Use Different Strategies

Solve. Use the write-an-equation strategy.

1. At To-Go Pizza, each pizza costs $12 and each small salad costs $2. A delivery charge of $3 is added to every order. How much would it cost to have 6 pizzas and 3 small salads delivered?

2. At the art supply store, pastels cost $2.25, drawing pads cost $6.50, and pencils cost $1.17. Kelly bought 3 pastels, 2 drawing pads, and 12 pencils. How much money did Kelly spend?

3. Myra orders 3 beach balls and 2 sand castle kits from a catalog. The price of each beach ball is $4. The price of each sand castle kit is $10. Shipping costs for Myra's order are $6. What is the total cost of the order, including shipping?

4. Use the equation $S = n(n + 1)$ to find the sum of consecutive even numbers through 40.

Solve. Use the guess-and-test strategy combined with any other strategies you want to use. Use a table to show your work.

5. Molly walked 6 more miles than Jeff on Sunday. They walked a total of 22 miles. How far did Jeff walk?

6. A DVD rental service keeps a record of the types of movies customers rent each day. Customers rented a total of 1,280 adventure movies and comedies on Saturday. They rented 19 times as many adventure movies as comedies. How many adventure movies did they rent on Saturday?

TRY IT

Choose and Use Strategies (C)

Practice Using Strategies

WORK BACKWARD

When you're given the "final" piece of information, you can often work backward to solve a story problem. You can use arrows and a set of steps to show how you worked backward from the last piece of information to find the answer.

Dacia has twice as many plants as Carol. Carol has 3 more plants than Sharon. Sharon has 2 fewer plants than Emily. Emily has 19 plants. How many plants does Dacia have?

Dacia has 40 plants.	←	Multiply by 2 to find how many plants Dacia has.	←	Add 3 to find how many plants Carol has.	←	Subtract 2 to find how many plants Sharon has.	←	Start with the number of plants Emily has.
		$20 \cdot 2 = 40$		$17 + 3 = 20$		$19 - 2 = 17$		19

Work backward to solve. Show your work using arrows and a set of steps.

1. David bought 3 more apples than oranges. He bought twice as many bananas as oranges, and he bought 5 more plums than bananas. David bought 17 plums. How many apples did David buy?

2. Ruby was selling melons at her fruit stand. She sold 13 melons in the morning. At lunchtime, 16 more melons were delivered to her. She then sold 19 more melons. At the end of the day, she had 11 melons left. How many melons did Ruby have at the start of the day?

TRY IT

Use any strategy you have learned to solve. Name the strategy.
Show your work.

3. Percy bought 3 bottles of fruit juice and 2 packages of crackers. Bottles of fruit juice cost $1.49 each. Packages of crackers cost $0.89 each. How much did Percy spend?

4. Keiko has 3 more quarters than dimes. She has 2 times as many nickels as dimes. She has $2.00 in quarters. How much money does Keiko have?

5. Rachael's soccer game starts at 11 a.m. Her coach wants her to arrive 20 minutes before the game starts. It takes her 15 minutes to get to the game. She needs $1\frac{1}{2}$ hours to eat breakfast, get ready, and do her chores. What is the latest time that Rachael can get up in the morning so that she gets to her game on time?

Choose the answer.

6. Alex can read 22 pages of his book in an hour. How many pages can Alex read in 4.35 hours?

   A. **Substitute simpler numbers.**

   Suppose that Alex can read 20 pages in 1 hour. Calculate how many pages he could read in 4 hours: $20 \cdot 4 = 80$. So in 4 hours he can read 80 pages. Now that you have figured out how to solve the problem, go back and solve it using fractions.

   B. **Work backward.**

   Start with 4.25 hours. Subtract 22 pages to see how many sets of 22 are in 4.25 hours.

   C. **Make a table.**

   Look for a pattern in your table.

Hour	1	2	3	4	5	6
Pages	22	22	22	22	22	22

T R Y   I T

Solve Simple to Complex Problems (A)

Solve One-Step Story Problems

Worked Examples

You can use the problem-solving plan to solve simple one-step story problems with mixed numbers.

PROBLEM 1 Billy ran $1\frac{3}{4}$ miles on Monday and $2\frac{1}{2}$ miles on Tuesday. How many miles did he run in all?

SOLUTION

UNDERSTAND THE PROBLEM

List the important numbers in the problem and figure out what operations you will use. The important numbers are $1\frac{3}{4}$ and $2\frac{1}{2}$. You will use addition.

DEVISE A PLAN

Write an equation. Compare the denominators in the mixed numbers to see if one or both of them need to be changed.

CARRY OUT THE PLAN

1 Write the equation. The variable n represents the total miles run. $\longrightarrow$ $1\frac{3}{4} + 2\frac{1}{2} = n$

2 Find the least common denominator (LCD) of the fractions $\frac{3}{4}$ and $\frac{1}{2}$. The LCD of the two fractions is 4. $\longrightarrow$ $\frac{1}{2} = \frac{2}{4}$

3 Change $2\frac{1}{2}$ to $2\frac{2}{4}$ in the equation and add. $\longrightarrow$ $1\frac{3}{4} + 2\frac{2}{4} = 3\frac{5}{4}$

4 Simplify. $\longrightarrow$ $3\frac{5}{4} = 4\frac{1}{4}$

LOOK BACK

Check that the answer makes sense. You can estimate that Billy ran about 2 miles each day, so the answer should be about 4 miles.

ANSWER Billy ran a total of $4\frac{1}{4}$ miles Monday and Tuesday.

Solve. Express in simplest mixed-number form.

1. The Kelly family went shopping. They drove for $3\frac{1}{2}$ miles to one store and $2\frac{3}{4}$ miles to another store. How many miles did they drive in all?

2. Colin hiked for $3\frac{2}{3}$ miles one weekend. The next weekend, he hiked for $2\frac{2}{3}$ miles. How many miles did he hike?

You can use the problem-solving plan to solve more complex one-step story problems with fractions and mixed numbers in the same way you solved the simpler problems.

PROBLEM 2 Steve likes to ride his bike on a trail near his home. He lives $\frac{7}{10}$ of a mile from a bike trail. On Saturday, he rode $2\frac{1}{2}$ miles. On Sunday, he rode $3\frac{2}{3}$ miles. On Monday, he rode $3\frac{4}{6}$ miles. How far did Steve ride in all?

SOLUTION

UNDERSTAND THE PROBLEM

This problem is more complex than the problem in the previous Worked Example, but you can use the same method to solve it.

The important numbers in this problem are $2\frac{1}{2}$, $3\frac{2}{3}$, and $3\frac{4}{6}$. You will use addition.

DEVISE A PLAN

As in the previous Worked Example, you can solve this problem by writing an equation.

CARRY OUT THE PLAN

1 Write the equation. The variable n represents the total miles ridden. $\longrightarrow$ $2\frac{1}{2} + 3\frac{2}{3} + 3\frac{4}{6} = n$

2 Find the least common denominator (LCD) of the fractions $\frac{1}{2}$, $\frac{2}{3}$, and $\frac{4}{6}$. The LCD is 6. $\longrightarrow$ $\frac{3}{6}, \frac{4}{6}, \frac{4}{6}$

3 Put the equivalent mixed numbers in the equation and add. $\longrightarrow$ $2\frac{3}{6} + 3\frac{4}{6} + 3\frac{4}{6} = 8\frac{11}{6}$

4 Simplify. $\longrightarrow$ $8\frac{11}{6} = 9\frac{5}{6}$

LOOK BACK

Check that the answer makes sense. You can estimate that Steve rode about $2\frac{1}{2}$, $3\frac{1}{2}$, and $3\frac{1}{2}$ miles for a total of about $9\frac{1}{2}$ miles. The exact answer is close to that estimate.

ANSWER Steve rode $9\frac{5}{6}$ miles during the 3 days.

Solve. Express in simplest mixed-number form.

3. Tara's soccer team went out for pizza. They ate $8\frac{2}{3}$ pizzas. Last week, they ate $6\frac{3}{9}$ pizzas. How many more pizzas did they eat this week?

4. Peter's team went out to eat twice after games. Both times, the team ate 24-inch sandwiches. The first week, they ate $3\frac{1}{2}$ sandwiches. The second week, they ate $4\frac{7}{10}$ sandwiches. How many more sandwiches did they eat the second week than the first week?

L E A R N

Solve Simple to Complex Problems (A)

Solve Multistep Story Problems

You can use the problem-solving plan to solve simple multistep story problems with fractions and mixed numbers.

PROBLEM 1 Every week, Tommy buys $1\frac{1}{3}$ pounds of turkey and $2\frac{2}{3}$ pounds of cheese. How much turkey and cheese would he buy in 6 weeks?

SOLUTION

UNDERSTAND THE PROBLEM
Find the important numbers in the problem and figure out what operations you will use. The important numbers are $1\frac{1}{3}$, $2\frac{2}{3}$, and 6. You will use addition and multiplication. You might restate the problem as follows: If Tommy buys $1\frac{1}{3}$ pounds plus $2\frac{2}{3}$ pounds of those food items each week for 6 weeks, how many total pounds would he buy?

DEVISE A PLAN
Write an equation. Change the mixed numbers to improper fractions. Add them. Multiply the sum by 6.

CARRY OUT THE PLAN

1. Write an equation. The variable *n* represents the total amount of food in 1 week. ⟶ $1\frac{1}{3} + 2\frac{2}{3} = n$

2. Add. ⟶ $1\frac{1}{3} + 2\frac{2}{3} = 4$

3. Write another equation. The variable *n* represents ⟶ $n = 4 \cdot 6$ the total amount of food in 6 weeks.

4. Multiply. ⟶ $n = 24$

LOOK BACK
Double-check the math and look at the story problem to see if the answer is reasonable. A quick estimate would be $(1 + 3)6$, or 24, which is also the exact answer.

ANSWER Tommy would buy 24 pounds of turkey and cheese in 6 weeks.

You can use the problem-solving plan to solve more complex multistep story problems with fractions and mixed numbers in the same way you solved the simpler problems.

PROBLEM 2 Tommy bought $2\frac{8}{10}$ pounds of cheddar cheese. He bought $1\frac{6}{8}$ fewer pounds of American cheese than cheddar cheese. He bought the same amount of the same cheeses for 5 weeks. How much American cheese did he buy in 5 weeks?

SOLUTION

UNDERSTAND THE PROBLEM

Find the important numbers in the problem and figure out what operations you will use. The important numbers are $2\frac{8}{10}$, $1\frac{6}{8}$, and 5. You will use subtraction and multiplication.

DEVISE A PLAN

Subtract to find out how much American cheese Tommy buys each week and then multiply that amount over 5 weeks.

Refer to the simpler problems in the previous Worked Example. This problem is similar but has more steps.

CARRY OUT THE PLAN

1 Find out how many pounds of American cheese Tommy bought each week.

- Write equation. The variable n represents the total amount of American cheese in 1 week. $\longrightarrow$ $2\frac{8}{10} - 1\frac{6}{8} = n$

- Find the least common denominator for the mixed numbers. $\rightarrow$ $2\frac{32}{40} - 1\frac{30}{40} = n$

- Subtract the whole numbers and the fractions. $\longrightarrow$ $2\frac{32}{40} - 1\frac{30}{40} = 1\frac{2}{40}$

- Simplify. $\longrightarrow$ $1\frac{2}{40} = 1\frac{1}{20}$

Tommy bought $1\frac{1}{20}$ pounds of American cheese every week.

2 Find out how many pounds of American cheese Tommy bought over 5 weeks.

- Write equation. The variable n represents the total amount of American cheese in 5 weeks. $\longrightarrow$ $1\frac{1}{20} \cdot 5 = n$

- Change the mixed number to an improper fraction. $\longrightarrow$ $\frac{21}{20} \cdot \frac{5}{1} = n$

- Multiply. $\longrightarrow$ $\frac{21}{4} \cdot \frac{1}{1} = \frac{21}{4}$

- Simplify. $\longrightarrow$ $\frac{21}{4} = 5\frac{1}{4}$

LEARN

Solve. Express in simplest mixed-number form.

1. Katie buys $2\frac{2}{4}$ pounds of grapes and $1\frac{1}{3}$ pounds of pears each week. How much fruit would she buy in 4 weeks?

2. In January, Betsy volunteered for $5\frac{3}{4}$ hours at the library. In February, she volunteered $1\frac{2}{3}$ fewer hours. In March, she volunteered $4\frac{1}{2}$ more hours than in February. How many hours did she volunteer in March?

3. Adam ran the same amount each day for 4 days. He ran a total of $7\frac{1}{5}$ miles. The first day, he also walked $2\frac{3}{8}$ miles. How far did he run and walk on the first day?

LEARN

Solve Simple to Complex Problems (B)
Fractions as Decimals in Story Problems

Worked Examples

You can use the problem-solving plan to solve story problems that include changing fractions and mixed numbers to decimal numbers.

PROBLEM Sophia bought $3\frac{1}{5}$ meters of ribbon. Ribbon costs $1.05 a meter. How much did Sophia spend?

SOLUTION

UNDERSTAND THE PROBLEM
Restate the problem by saying that Sophia bought $3\frac{1}{5}$ meters of ribbon for $1.05 a meter. You need to know how much she spent on ribbon. The operation you will use is multiplication.

DEVISE A PLAN
Figure out how to change the mixed number to a decimal number. Then write equations so you can multiply the decimal number you computed by the one already in the problem ($1.05) and solve the problem.

CARRY OUT THE PLAN

1 Change $3\frac{1}{5}$ to a decimal number.

$$3\frac{1}{5} = 3.2$$

2 Use the variable n to represent the money Sophia spent. Write an equation.

$$n = 3.2 \cdot \$1.05$$

$$n = \$3.36$$

LOOK BACK
Make sure that the answer is reasonable. For an estimate, think: Sophia bought about 3 meters of ribbon for about $1.00 a meter for a total cost of $3.00, so the answer of $3.36 is reasonable.

ANSWER Sophia spent $3.36 on ribbon.

L E A R N

Solve.

1. Jenny bought $2\frac{1}{2}$ yards of blue ribbon and $4\frac{3}{4}$ yards of yellow ribbon. The ribbon costs $1.50 a yard. How much did Jenny spend on ribbon?

2. Sam needed flannel to make a blanket for his parents. He bought $1\frac{1}{4}$ yards of purple flannel and $1\frac{3}{6}$ yards of black flannel. The flannel costs $2.40 a yard. How much did Sam spend on flannel?

3. Kevin bought decorative ribbon for a parade. He got to the store at 7:00 p.m., and it took him 15 minutes to check out. He bought $5\frac{1}{5}$ meters of purple polka-dot ribbon and $6\frac{1}{4}$ meters of red-and-white striped ribbon. The decorative ribbon costs $2.60 a meter. How much did Kevin spend on ribbon?

4. Amy bought fabric to make curtains. She bought $2\frac{1}{4}$ feet for one window and $3\frac{3}{12}$ feet for another window. She will be using blinds on her other three windows, which measure $3\frac{1}{5}$ feet, $3\frac{1}{2}$ feet, and $2\frac{3}{8}$ feet. The fabric for her curtains costs $8.15 a foot. How much did Amy spend on fabric?

LEARN

Solve Simple to Complex Problems (B)
Convert Measurements in Story Problems

Worked Examples

You can use the problem-solving plan to solve multistep story problems that include converting one unit of measure to another.

PROBLEM Martin filled canteens with $3\frac{8}{10}$ gallons of water for his hiking group to drink during a hike. One gallon of water weighs about 8.35 pounds. How many pounds of water did Martin's hiking group take on the hike?

SOLUTION

UNDERSTAND THE PROBLEM

- Ask yourself what you need to find, explain, or show. You need to find the number of pounds of water Martin's hiking group took, and you need to convert gallons to pounds to get the answer.
- Restate the problem. Martin's hiking group took $3\frac{8}{10}$ gallons of water at about 8.35 pounds per gallon, and you will find out how many pounds of water the group took on the hike.
- Figure out what operation to use. You will use multiplication.

DEVISE A PLAN

To solve the problem, change $3\frac{8}{10}$ to a decimal number because the weight of the water is given as a decimal number. Then multiply the number of gallons of water by the weight of 1 gallon of water.

CARRY OUT THE PLAN

1 Change $3\frac{8}{10}$ to a decimal number. $3\frac{8}{10} = 3.8$

2 Recall that 1 gallon of water weighs about 8.35 pounds. Let n represent the amount of water Martin's hiking group took on the hike.

$n = 3.8 \cdot 8.35$

$n = 31.73$

LOOK BACK

Make sure that the answer is reasonable. For an estimate, think: $3\frac{8}{10}$ gallons is close to 4 gallons, and 8.35 pounds is close to 8 pounds: $4 \cdot 8 = 32$. So the answer of 31.73 is reasonable.

ANSWER Martin's hiking group took about 31.73 pounds of water on the hike.

LEARN

Solve.

1. Bella and her family are at a picnic. She brought a jug filled with $2\frac{9}{10}$ gallons of water. Her uncle brought another jug that held $4\frac{7}{10}$ gallons of water. One gallon of water weighs about 8.35 pounds. Bella's aunt brought $\frac{1}{4}$ gallon of water. How many pounds of water did Bella and her uncle bring to the picnic?

2. Kelsey has two music playlists on her MP3 player that she wants to combine. The first playlist is 12 minutes and 51 seconds long. The second is 15 minutes and 38 seconds. The songs on the playlists average 3 minutes and 15 seconds. How many seconds of music will Kelsey have when she combines the two playlists? (Hint: 1 minute = 60 seconds)

3. Mary's family is making a macaroni-and-cheese dish and homemade ice cream for a team picnic. Each batch of macaroni and cheese calls for $2\frac{1}{2}$ cups of milk. Each batch of ice cream calls for $3\frac{1}{4}$ cups of milk. Her family needs to make 4 batches of each. How many quarts of milk does Mary's family need? (Hint: 1 quart = 4 cups)

4. Paul's family is going to the soccer team party. They are taking $1\frac{3}{4}$ pounds of fruit salad for each family and $\frac{1}{4}$ pounds of bagel chips for each family. There are 12 families. Each family has at least 4 people and at least 1 boy. How many ounces of fruit salad and bagel chips will Paul's family take to the party? (Hint: 16 ounces = 1 pound)

LEARN

Use the information in this scenario to answer all the questions.

A trucker is planning her next trip across several states. She has plenty of time to deliver her haul, so she is looking at data to determine whether to take the back roads, which are more scenic, or the interstate, which is faster. She can average 55 miles per hour on the back roads and 70 miles per hour on the interstate.

1. Use the general equation distance = rate • time to write one equation to represent the data for the back roads and another equation to represent the interstate data. (Use d_b to represent the distance on the back roads and d_i for the distance on the interstate.)

2. Copy the table and enter the missing values. Show your work.

Time (h)	Distance for back roads (mi)	Distance for interstate (mi)
5	275	350
10	550	700
15	(a)	1,050
20	1,100	(b)
25	(c)	(d)
30	1,650	2,100

3. Use the same pair of axes to graph at least 3 points for each set of data. Draw lines through the points for each graph. (Place the label b at the end of the line for the back roads data and the label i at the end of the line for the interstate data.)

4. The driver receives a notice that the actual distance of the first part of her trip will be 1,925 miles.

   (a) How many hours will this trip take on the back roads? Show your work.

   (b) How many hours will this trip take on the interstate? Show your work.

T R Y   I T

5. Use your answers to Problems 1, 2, or 3 to answer these questions. Show all of your work.

   (a) How long would a 1,540-mile trip take the driver on the back roads?

   (b) How many miles can the driver cover on the interstate in 37 hours?

   (c) If the driver wanted to cover 2,080 miles in 32 hours, what rate of speed will she need to average?

Think Like a Mathematician Self-Check

6. State the actions and thinking you used during this lesson as a math learner.

Math Thinking and Actions
I made sense of problems by • Explaining to myself what a problem means and what it asks for • Using drawings or diagrams to represent a problem I was solving
I explained my math thinking clearly.
I tried out new ways to check if an answer is reasonable.
Other

Solve Problems Logically

Solve Equal-Measures Problems

Worked Examples

You can use the problem-solving plan to solve story problems about items or measurements that are equally grouped, also known as equal-measures problems.

PROBLEM Susan bought 50 inches of red ribbon and 20 inches of white ribbon. She wants to use equal amounts of both types of ribbon in 5 projects. What is the difference in length between one piece of red ribbon and one piece of white ribbon?

SOLUTION

UNDERSTAND THE PROBLEM
You know the length of the red ribbon and the white ribbon and that they are each divided into equal-sized pieces. You know that both colors of ribbon are shared among 5 projects. You need to find out the difference in length between the two colors of ribbon.

If you were to restate the problem in your own words, you might say this: Share 50 inches of red ribbon and 20 inches of white ribbon among 5 projects by separating each color of ribbon into equal-sized pieces. Find out the difference in length between a piece of red ribbon and a piece of white ribbon.

DEVISE A PLAN
Use equations to solve the problem. Divide the total amount of red ribbon by 5. Divide the total amount of white ribbon by 5. Subtract the lesser quotient from the greater one.

CARRY OUT THE PLAN

1. Find the length of each piece of red ribbon. $50 \div 5 = 10$

2. Find the length of each piece of white ribbon. $20 \div 5 = 4$

3. Subtract the lesser amount from the greater amount. $10 - 4 = 6$

LOOK BACK
Check that the answer is reasonable and that clear and logical steps were used to find the solution. Susan bought a little more than twice as much red ribbon as white ribbon, so it makes sense that one piece of red ribbon is a little more than twice as long as one piece of white ribbon.

ANSWER The difference in length between one piece of red ribbon and one piece of white ribbon is 6 inches.

LEARN

Write a sequence of steps to solve the problem.

1. Mr. Keefer is a truck driver. He drives 450 miles a day, 250 days each year. His truck can drive 15 miles on each gallon of gas. How many gallons of gas does Mr. Keefer's truck use each year?

2. Tommy is having snacks with his friends. Among the friends, 7 want to eat raisins and 5 want to eat banana chips. Raisins and banana chips are sold in 3-ounce bags. How many more ounces of raisins than banana chips will Tommy's friends eat?

3. Cindy bought 120 grams of chicken and 212 grams of turkey. She wants to divide each type of meat into 4 equal servings. What is the difference in mass between one serving of chicken and one serving of turkey?

4. Kim bought 2 feet of pine wood at $4.82 per foot. She also bought 4 feet of maple wood at $3.17 per foot. What is the total cost of Kim's purchases?

Estimation and Reasonable Answers

Reasonable Answers

Worked Examples

You can use the problem-solving plan to help you decide if an answer is reasonable.

PROBLEM Samantha read the following problem:

- Mr. Miller has driving directions from his home to a hardware store. The store opens at 8:00 a.m. The directions tell him to drive on Elm Street for $3\frac{7}{10}$ miles, turn right, and then drive on North Street for $3\frac{1}{5}$ miles to reach the store. What is the total distance from Mr. Miller's home to the hardware store?

Samantha calculated the answer this way: $3\frac{7}{10} + 3\frac{1}{5} = 3\frac{9}{10}$.

Is her answer reasonable?

SOLUTION

UNDERSTAND THE PROBLEM
To restate the problem, you could say that you need to find out if $3\frac{9}{10}$ is a reasonable answer to the story problem. The story problem asks for the total distance of Mr. Miller's drive. The distances given in the story problem are $3\frac{7}{10}$ and $3\frac{1}{5}$. The problem gives information that you don't need. You don't need to know when the store opens.

DEVISE A PLAN
For your plan, start by checking Samantha's plan. See if you agree with addition as the operation. You can then use a number line to estimate the answer to see if Samantha's answer is reasonable.

CARRY OUT THE PLAN

1 Note that Samantha used addition to solve the problem. Addition seems reasonable because the directions say Mr. Miller will drive some miles and then drive more miles. Samantha added $3\frac{7}{10}$ miles and $3\frac{1}{5}$ miles to get $3\frac{9}{10}$ miles.

L E A R N

2 Look at a number line from 2 to 8 in intervals of $\frac{1}{4}$, such as 2, $2\frac{1}{4}$, $2\frac{1}{2}$, $2\frac{3}{4}$, 3, and so on.

Number line from 2 to 8:
2 $2\frac{1}{4}$ $2\frac{1}{2}$ $2\frac{3}{4}$ 3 $3\frac{1}{4}$ $3\frac{1}{2}$ $3\frac{3}{4}$ 4 $4\frac{1}{4}$ $4\frac{1}{2}$ $4\frac{3}{4}$ 5 $5\frac{1}{4}$ $5\frac{1}{2}$ $5\frac{3}{4}$ 6 $6\frac{1}{4}$ $6\frac{1}{2}$ $6\frac{3}{4}$ 7 $7\frac{1}{4}$ $7\frac{1}{2}$ $7\frac{3}{4}$ 8

- The closest benchmark number greater than $3\frac{7}{10}$ is $3\frac{3}{4}$. Locate $3\frac{3}{4}$ on the number line.

- The closest benchmark number greater than $3\frac{1}{5}$ is $3\frac{1}{4}$. Count $3\frac{1}{4}$ units beyond $3\frac{3}{4}$. You end up at 7 on the number line.

- The estimated sum of $3\frac{7}{10}$ and $3\frac{1}{5}$ is 7, so the estimated distance from Mr. Miller's home to the hardware store is 7 miles.

3 Remember that Samantha's answer was $3\frac{9}{10}$ miles. Your estimate was 7 miles. Something's not right. Her answer is not reasonable.

4 Check the math in Samantha's solution.

Add the two distances: $3\frac{7}{10} + 3\frac{1}{5} = 3\frac{7}{10} + 3\frac{2}{10} = 6\frac{9}{10}$.

Samantha added the fractions together but forgot to add **both** of the whole-number parts, 3 and 3. She only added one whole number.

LOOK BACK

Review that Samantha's answer, $3\frac{9}{10}$, is not reasonable. Your estimate was 7, and those two numbers are not reasonably close. You used the number line to estimate that 7 was the answer. Your exact answer is $6\frac{9}{10}$, so your estimate and the exact answer are close. In fact, if you round the exact answer, $6\frac{9}{10}$, to the nearest whole number, it rounds to 7, which is the same as the estimate. So your answer makes sense and is reasonable.

ANSWER Samantha's answer isn't reasonable. The exact answer is $6\frac{9}{10}$ miles.

LEARN

Use estimation to find out if the answer is reasonable. Explain.

1. Hector read this problem:

   Patsy is making trail mix. She needs $4\frac{1}{2}$ cups of granola, $1\frac{2}{7}$ cups of raisins, and $\frac{5}{6}$ cup of chocolate chips for each batch. How many more cups of granola than raisins does she need?

   Hector calculated the answer this way: $4\frac{1}{2} - 1\frac{2}{7} = 3\frac{3}{14}$.

   Is his answer reasonable?

2. Anna solved this problem and said the answer was $7\frac{7}{8}$ feet:

   Molly had a piece of lace $4\frac{3}{4}$ feet long. She used $1\frac{1}{8}$ feet for a sewing project and gave her sister $2\frac{1}{4}$ feet to use on a pillow. How much lace did Molly have left?

   Is Anna's answer reasonable?

3. Jack solved this problem and said the answer was $1\frac{1}{10}$ feet:

   Trent cut two pieces of wood. One piece of wood was $3\frac{4}{5}$ feet long. He also cut a piece of wood that was $4\frac{7}{10}$ feet long. What was the total length of both pieces of wood?

   Is Jack's answer reasonable?

L E A R N

Measurements in Story Problems

Nature Story Problems

To solve this story problem, read the problem, answer questions about the problem, and then solve the problem.

PROBLEM A thirsty Asian elephant can drink 59 gallons of water.

What operation can you use to find how many gallons 3 elephants can drink?

What number sentence can you use to solve the problem?

How many gallons can 3 thirsty Asian elephants drink?

SOLUTION You know 1 Asian elephant can drink 59 gallons of water. To find how many gallons 3 Asian elephants can drink, you multiply.

$3 \times 59 = ?$

ANSWER multiply; $3 \times 59 = ?$; 177 gallons

Read the problem, answer the questions about the problem, and then solve the problem.

1. Baby camels, called calves, grow to full size in about 6 years. Suppose 5 adult camels have a mass of 2,500 kilograms altogether and they have equal mass.

   What operation can you use to find the mass of 1 camel?

   What number sentence can you use to solve the problem?

   What is the mass of 1 camel?

LEARN

Solve.

2. A blue whale calf can drink 128 gallons of milk per day.

    How many quarts of milk are in 128 gallons?

    How many quarts of milk can 3 blue whale calves drink in one day?

3. Adult humpback whales can eat 3,000 pounds of food a day.

    How many pounds of food can 12 humpback whales
    eat in a day?

    How many ounces of food can 1 humpback whale eat in a day?

4. A line of ants is 980 millimeters long. If each ant is 7 millimeters long,
    how many ants are in the line?

    How many centimeters long is the line? There are 10 millimeters in
    1 centimeter.

5. Carpenter ants live outside in mountains as high as 9,000 feet.

    How many inches and how many yards are in 9,000 feet?

Organize Data to Draw Histograms (A)

Organize Data in a Frequency Table

Worked Examples

You can record data in a frequency table as one way to organize and display data.

PROBLEM In a survey, people were asked how old they had been when they learned to ride a bike. Their replies are in this table. Create a frequency table with these data.

SOLUTION

1 To make a frequency table, draw a table with three columns. Put a title at the top. Label the columns.

- Name ranges in the first column, "Age range."
- Write tally marks to record the data in the middle column, "Tally."
- Record the frequency of the data in the third column, "Frequency."

2 Decide on the age ranges for rows in the first column. You can have age ranges of 7–10, 11–14, and 15–28. You can have more age ranges if you want to have more rows.

3 Start at the top left-hand side of the data table. Make a tally mark in the middle column of the frequency table for each age data point. Put the tally mark in the correct "Age range" row.

4 After you have finished, count the tally marks in each row. That number is the frequency. Write the frequency for each row in the third column.

Age When Learned to Ride a Bike			
28	13	11	9
20	13	11	9
18	13	10	8
16	13	10	8
15	12	10	8
13	12	9	7
13	12	9	7

ANSWER

Age When Learned to Ride a Bike		
Age range	**Tally**	**Frequency**
7–10	卌 卌 II	12
11–14	卌 卌 I	11
15–28	卌	5

LEARN

Follow the directions to complete the activity.

1. Create a frequency table for the data. Write a title and column headings. Put the frequency data in the table. Group the heights so you have one column with ranges of numbers in a logical sequence, such as 60–79, 80–99, 100–119, and so on. In the second column, use tally marks to record the number of heights within the ranges. In the third column, write the frequency number.

Tall Ferris Wheels			
Ferris wheel	Height (m)	Ferris wheel	Height (m)
Beijing Great Wheel	208	Harbin Ferris Wheel	110
Great Berlin Wheel	175	Jinjiang Park Ferris Wheel	108
Singapore Flyer	165	HEP Five	106
Star of Nanchang	160	Grande Roue de Paris	100
London Eye	135	Space Eye	100
Suzhou Ferris Wheel	120	The Great Wheel	94
The Southern Star	120	Aurora Wheel	90
Tianjin Eye	120	Eurowheel	90
Changsha Ferris Wheel	120	Janfusun Fancyworld	88
Zhengzhou Ferris Wheel	120	Mashhad Fun Fair	80
Sky Dream Fukuoka	120	The Ferris Wheel (original Ferris wheel)	80
Diamond and Flowers Ferris Wheel	117	Moscow-850	75
Sky Wheel of Odaiba	115	Polaris Tower	72
Star of Tai Lake	115	Miramar Ferris Wheel	70
Cosmo Clock 21	112.5	Texas Star	65
Tempozan Harbor Village Ferris Wheel	112.5	Riesenrad Vienna	64.8

LEARN

Organize Data to Draw Histograms (A)

Work with Frequency Tables

Follow the directions to complete the activity.

1. Create a frequency table for the data.
   - Write a title and column headings.
   - Put the frequency data in the table. Group the number of books people read so the first column has ranges of numbers in a logical sequence. Use 5-book ranges starting with 1–5, 6–10, and so on.
   - In the second column, use tally marks to record the number of people within the ranges.
   - In the third column, write the frequency number.

Book Club	
Name	Number of books read in September, October, and November
Betty	12
David	4
Sonia	2
Sophia	15
Steven	7
Paul	9
Bob	20
Marcia	21
Mary	16
Rob	3
Eric	14
Mark	9
Brian	14
Carl	20
Jared	6

TRY IT

Choose the answer.

2. Maurice recorded the number of minutes he did yard work each week for 6 weeks. Which frequency table shows the data?

Week 1: 45 minutes
Week 2: 65 minutes
Week 3: 110 minutes
Week 4: 75 minutes
Week 5: 60 minutes
Week 6: 30 minutes

A.

Yard Work

Time (min)	Tally	Frequency
0–19	|	1
20–39		0
40–59	||	2
60–79	||	2
80–99		0
100–119	|	1

B.

Yard Work

Time (min)	Tally	Frequency
0–19	|	1
20–39	|	1
40–59	|||	3
60–79	|	1
80–99		0
100–119		0

C.

Yard Work

Time (min)	Tally	Frequency
0–19		0
20–39	|	1
40–59	|	1
60–79	|||	3
80–99		0
100–119	|	1

TRY IT

Choose the answer.

3. Lara recorded the number of hours she exercised each month for a year. Which frequency table shows the data?

January: 8 hours   July: 22 hours
February: 7 hours   August: 8 hours
March: 10 hours   September: 10 hours
April: 8 hours   October: 9 hours
May: 14 hours   November: 11 hours
June: 20 hours   December: 6 hours

A.

Exercise		
Time (h)	Tally	Frequency
0–4		0
5–9	|||||	5
10–14	|||||	5
15–19			1
20–24			1

B.

Exercise		
Time (h)	Tally	Frequency
0–4		0
5–9	||||||	6
10–14	||||	4
15–19		0
20–24	||	2

C.

Exercise		
Time (h)	Tally	Frequency
0–4	||||||	6
5–9		0
10–14	|||	3
15–19		0
20–24	|||	3

TRY IT

4. Deborah recorded the number of servings of fruit that each member of her ballet class ate in a week. Which frequency table shows the data?

Helen: 15

Jane: 9

Gillian: 13

Danielle: 19

Nina: 8

Sally: 17

Vanessa: 18

Claire: 13

Zoe: 12

A.

Fruit Eaten in a Week		
Number	**Tally**	**Frequency**
0–5		0
6–10	||	2
11–15	||||	4
16–20	|||	3
21–25		0

B.

Fruit Eaten in a Week		
Number	**Tally**	**Frequency**
0–5		0
6–10	|||	3
11–15	|||	3
16–20	|||	3
21–25	|||	3

C.

Fruit Eaten in a Week		
Number	**Tally**	**Frequency**
0–5	|	1
6–10	||	2
11–15	||||	4
16–20	|||	3
21–25		0

TRY IT

Organize Data to Draw Histograms (B)

Make a Histogram

Worked Examples

A histogram is a graph that displays the data from a frequency table. Histograms have bars that represent data. The bars are usually all the same width. The width depends on the range of measurements in the frequency table. The heights of the bars depend on the frequency data.

A histogram has a horizontal axis (the bottom line of the graph) and a vertical axis (the line along the left side of the graph). Each axis is labeled with a name and with numbers that are used for placement of the bars.

World's Longest Roller Coasters		
Length range (ft)	Tally	Frequency
2,000–4,000	|||	3
4,001–6,000	||||	4
6,001–8,000	⦀⦀ |	6
8,001–10,000	⦀⦀ ||	7
10,001–12,000	||	2

PROBLEM Draw a histogram to display the data in the frequency table.

SOLUTION

1 Write a title at the top of the histogram. The title should describe the data in the frequency table, such as "World's Longest Roller Coasters."

2 Label the horizontal axis and the vertical axis. For the horizontal axis label, write the column name for the range of measurements in the frequency table: "Length range (ft)." For the vertical axis label, write "Frequency."

3 Mark off 5 even sections along the horizontal axis for ranges and write the ranges from the frequency table below the axis. As you mark off the ranges, don't put space between them. The bars on a histogram sit right next to each other.

4 Number the vertical axis. Histograms often show one number greater than the greatest number in the frequency table. When the vertical axis includes one greater number, the scale is easier to read. The frequency table has frequencies from 0 to 7, so number the vertical axis from 0 to 8.

5 Draw a bar for the first range, 2,000–4,000. The frequency is 3, so the bar should stop at the 3 on the vertical axis. Using the data in the frequency table, draw and shade a bar for each range (each row in the frequency table should have one bar in the histogram). Use a ruler to draw the bars.

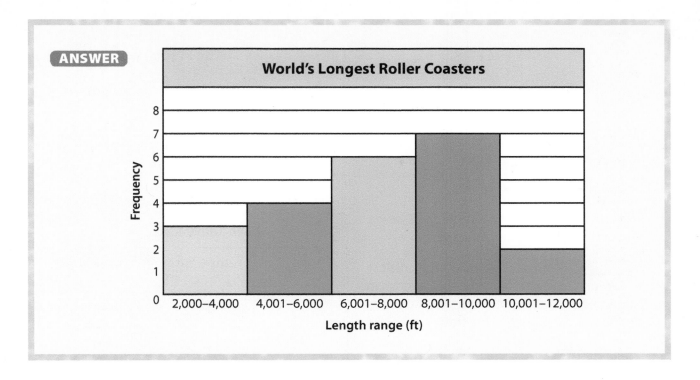

World's Longest Roller Coasters

Frequency

Length range (ft)

2,000–4,000   4,001–6,000   6,001–8,000   8,001–10,000   10,001–12,000

Follow the steps to draw a histogram to display the data in the frequency table.

1. Write a title at the top of the histogram.

2. Label the horizontal axis.

3. Number the vertical axis.

4. Write the ranges on the horizontal axis.

5. Draw and shade a bar for each range in the frequency table.

Tall Ferris Wheels		
Height range (m)	Tally	Frequency
60–79	卌	5
80–99	卌 I	6
100–119	卌 卌	10
120–139	卌 II	7
140–159		0
160–179	III	3
180–199		0
200–219	I	1

LEARN

Organize Data to Draw Histograms (B)

Make a Frequency Table and Histogram

Worked Examples

You can use the data in a table to create a frequency table and a histogram.

PROBLEM This table shows the coldest water temperatures at a lake for 2 weeks in December. Create a frequency table and a histogram to represent the data.

SOLUTION

1. For the frequency table, divide the data into ranges. Logical ranges would be 38.0–40.9, 41.0–43.9, and 44.0–46.9. Make the columns. Write the tally marks and the frequency numbers in the correct columns.

2. Use the frequency table to draw a histogram. On the horizontal axis, write the ranges from the frequency table. Number the vertical axis to show all the frequencies. Draw bars to represent the data.

Lake Temperatures		
Day	Temperature in Week 1 (°F)	Temperature in Week 2 (°F)
Sunday	44.0	38.7
Monday	41.5	38.2
Tuesday	39.2	40.0
Wednesday	39.5	42.1
Thursday	40.3	42.5
Friday	38.0	44.8
Saturday	39.6	45.1

ANSWER

Frequency Table

Lake Temperatures		
Temperature range (°F)	Tally	Frequency
38.0– 40.9	ⵌ |||	8
41.0– 43.9	|||	3
44.0– 46.9	|||	3

Histogram

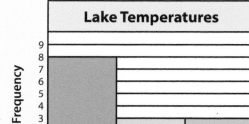

DATA ANALYSIS AND REPRESENTATION

ORGANIZE DATA TO DRAW HISTOGRAMS (B)

Use the table to answer the problems.

Frogtown is located in California between Yosemite National Park and Lake Tahoe, south of Historic Angels Camp. The table shows the Frog Jump Results data.

Frog Jump Results		
Frog's name	Frog jockey	Distance
Lisa Can Do	Brent	21 ft 4 in.
Jumpin' Daly	Joseph	20 ft 5 in.
To Be or Not to Be	Gavin	19 ft 10 in.
Kasha	Jacob	19 ft 6 in.
Don't You Wish	Bob	19 ft
Buck Shot	Michael	18 ft 9 in.
Worthless Chris	Craig	18 ft 6 in.
Papi	Kevin	18 ft 5 in.

Follow the steps to draw a frequency table to represent the data.

1. Give the frequency table a title. Label the columns.

2. Decide what the ranges will be. Write the ranges in the first column in ascending order.

3. Tally the data for each range. Write the tally marks in the middle column.

4. Count the tally marks for each row. Write the number for each row in the "Frequency" column.

Follow the steps to draw a histogram to display the data in the frequency table.

5. Write a title at the top of the histogram.

6. Label the horizontal axis.

7. Number the vertical axis.

8. Write the ranges on the horizontal axis.

9. Draw and shade a bar for each range in the frequency table.

LEARN

Organize Data to Draw Histograms (B)

Make and Interpret Histograms

Use the table to answer the problems. Follow the steps to draw a histogram to display the data in the frequency table.

Visitors to National Parks		
Numbers of visitors	Tally	Frequency
0–99,999	~~IIII~~ III	8
100,000–199,999	III	3
200,000 –299,999	II	2
300,000–399,999	III	3

1. Write a title at the top of the histogram.

2. Label the horizontal axis.

3. Number the vertical axis.

4. Write the ranges on the horizontal axis.

5. Draw and shade a bar for each range in the frequency table.

TRY IT

Choose the answer.

6. Nadia recorded the number of letters each person in her summer camp group sent home each week. She then organized the information in a frequency table.

Number of Letters Sent		
Number of letters	Tally	Frequency
0–2	卌 卌	10
3–5	卌	5
6–8	|||	3

Which histogram correctly displays this information?

A.
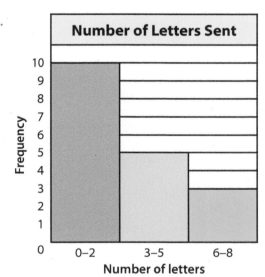

B.
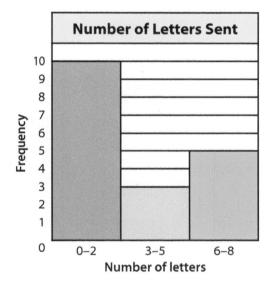

C.
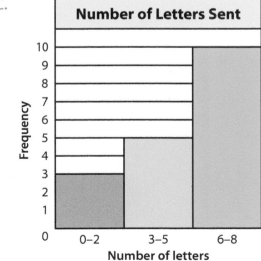

TRY IT

Choose the answer.

7. Dave recorded the number of runs he scored in each baseball game in one season. He then organized the information in a frequency table.

Runs Scored		
Runs	**Tally**	**Frequency**
0–3	|||	3
4–7	||	2
8–11			1

Which histogram correctly displays this information?

A.

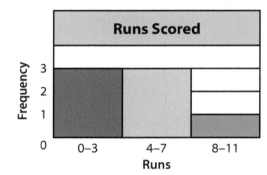

B.

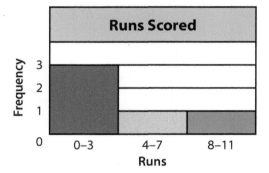

C.

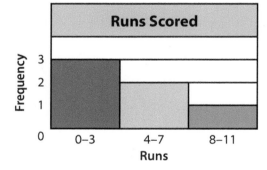

TRY IT

8. Bobbi recorded the number of points she scored in each basketball game she played during the summer. She then organized the information in a frequency table.

Points Scored		
Points	**Tally**	**Frequency**
0–9	|||	3
10–19	||||	4
20–29	||	2
30–39	|||||	5
40–49	||	2

Which histogram correctly displays this information?

A.

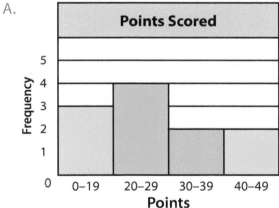

B.

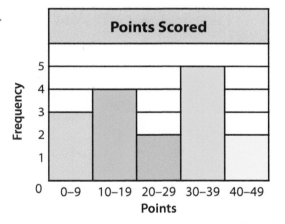

C.

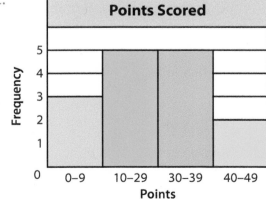

TRY IT

Create Circle Graphs

Organize Data on a Circle Graph

Worked Examples

You can use data to create a circle graph.

PROBLEM Students answered a survey on their favorite type of book: adventure, science fiction, or mystery. The students' responses were adventure, 25; science fiction, 20; and mystery, 5. Show the data in a circle graph that has a value of 1 for the entire circle and shows the fraction of the responses for each type of book.

SOLUTION

1 Find the sum of the data values: $25 + 20 + 5 = 50$. There were 50 students who took part in the survey.

2 Find a fraction to represent each data value. The denominator of each fraction will be 50 because 50 students took part in the survey. Then rewrite each fraction so that all the fractions have a common denominator.

- To represent 25 students, write $\frac{25}{50}$. $\frac{25}{50} = \frac{5}{10}$

- To represent 20 students, write $\frac{20}{50}$. $\frac{20}{50} = \frac{4}{10}$

- To represent 5 students, write $\frac{5}{50}$. $\frac{5}{50} = \frac{1}{10}$

3 Add to make sure the sum of the fractions is 1. $\frac{5}{10} + \frac{4}{10} + \frac{1}{10} = \frac{10}{10} = 1$

4 Using your ruler, divide your circle into $\frac{5}{10}, \frac{4}{10}$, and $\frac{1}{10}$ sections. It's acceptable to draw only approximate sizes for the sections. Always label your sections so that it's clear what fraction of the circle they represent.

- Start by drawing a line through the circle to divide it in half. Label one of the halves "adventure $\frac{5}{10}$."

- Then divide the other half into two sections, for $\frac{1}{10}$ and $\frac{4}{10}$. The $\frac{4}{10}$ section should look like it's about 4 times as large as the $\frac{1}{10}$ section. Label the sections "science fiction $\frac{4}{10}$" and "mystery $\frac{1}{10}$."

5 Write a title above the circle graph that accurately describes the data.

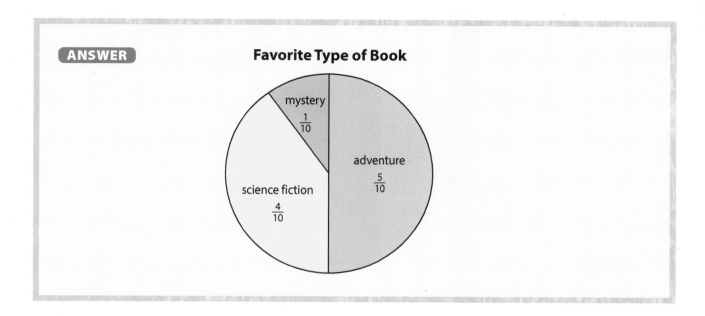

ANSWER

Favorite Type of Book

mystery $\frac{1}{10}$

adventure $\frac{5}{10}$

science fiction $\frac{4}{10}$

Use the data in the table to create a circle graph.

Students were surveyed about their favorite activities.

Favorite Activities	
Activity	**Number of students**
watching movies	20
playing with pets	80
reading	10
playing team sports	40
playing outdoors	10

1. Find the sum of the students surveyed.

2. Find the fraction of the circle that represents each value.

3. Divide the circle into fractional sections for the data points.

4. Write the description of the data and the value in each appropriate section of the circle graph. For this circle graph, label each section with the actual number of students and their favorite activity, rather than using the fraction as a label.

5. Write a title above the circle graph.

Use the data in the table to create a circle graph.

Kendall created a table to show how he spends his monthly allowance.

Monthly Allowance	
What money was used for	Amount
savings	$72
movies	$12
snacks	$6
charity	$6

6. Find the sum of the money amounts in Kendall's table.

7. Find a fraction to represent each value.

8. Divide the circle into fractional sections for the data points.

9. Write the description of the data and the value, in dollars, for each appropriate section of the circle graph.

10. Write a title above the circle graph.

Make a table and create a circle graph to represent the number of friends who like each type of movie best.

11. Nicole asked 36 friends what their favorite type of movie is. Nine said they liked comedies best. Eighteen said adventure movies were their favorite. The rest liked nature movies best.

Line Plots (A)

Create Line Plots with Fractions

Worked Examples

You can create a line plot to picture a group of values.

PROBLEM 1 The set of values are the time intervals in minutes between eruptions at Old Faithful Geyser in Yellowstone National Park. The time intervals are rounded to the nearest 5 minutes. Make a line plot for this data set.

65, 55, 55, 45, 80, 45, 65, 70, 60, 55, 90, 45, 60, 40, 55

SOLUTION

1 Look through the data set and find the greatest value and the least value. Create a number line and place the least value on the far left and the greatest value on the far right. Your number line may extend beyond the least and greatest values in the data set. Then place tick marks and labels at regular spaces between the least and greatest values, at intervals of 5.

2 Label the line plot with a title and a label for the values on the number line. Then place a mark above the number line according the first value, 65

Time Intervals Between Old Faithful Eruptions

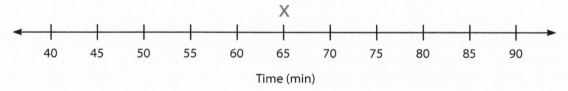

Time (min)

3 Place marks according to the rest of the data values in the set. If you have more than one mark at a location, arrange your marks so that they line up both across from each other and up and down.

L E A R N

Time Intervals Between Old Faithful Eruptions

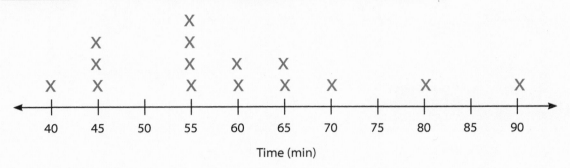

Time (min)

PROBLEM 2 A machine operator in a factory is trying to adjust a machine to make sure that the machine is making parts that are the correct weight. She has collected the following weights for the parts, in ounces. Create a line plot to display this data set.

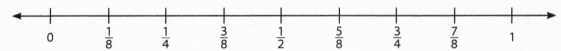

$$\frac{1}{4}, \frac{1}{8}, \frac{1}{2}, \frac{1}{8}, \frac{3}{8}, \frac{5}{8}, \frac{3}{8}, \frac{1}{8}, \frac{1}{4}, \frac{1}{4}, \frac{3}{4}, \frac{3}{8}, \frac{1}{4}, \frac{1}{2}, \frac{3}{8}, \frac{1}{4}, \frac{3}{8}, \frac{1}{2}, \frac{5}{8}, \frac{3}{8}$$

SOLUTION

1 Create the number line. In this case, since all the values are between 0 and 1, use 0 and 1 as the start and end values for the line plot. Then make tick marks at every one-eighth of an ounce. Remember that some of the values of the eighths will need to be put in simplest form, such as $\frac{2}{8} = \frac{1}{4}$.

2 Give the line plot a title and create a label for the numbers. Place a mark for each value in the data set. Make sure the number of marks matches the number of values. Remember to arrange your marks so that they line up both across from each other and up and down.

ANSWER

Part Weights

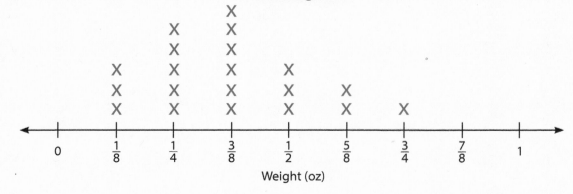

Weight (oz)

LEARN

Create a line plot for the data set in your Math Notebook. For data sets that provide information about the data, write a title for the line plot and provide an appropriate label with units for the numbers.

1. Students ran 100-yard sprints in gym class. Here are their individual times, in seconds:
12, 15, 13, 15, 18, 13, 12, 11, 15, 14, 19, 11, 12, 15, 14

2. $0, \frac{1}{5}, \frac{2}{5}, \frac{1}{5}, 0, \frac{3}{5}, 1, \frac{3}{5}, \frac{1}{5}, \frac{2}{5}, \frac{1}{5}, \frac{4}{5}, 0, \frac{3}{5}, \frac{4}{5}$

3. $\frac{1}{6}, \frac{1}{3}, \frac{1}{2}, \frac{1}{3}, \frac{1}{6}, \frac{1}{2}, \frac{2}{3}, \frac{1}{6}, \frac{2}{3}, \frac{1}{6}$

4. $\frac{2}{9}, \frac{1}{3}, \frac{1}{9}, \frac{4}{9}, \frac{2}{9}, \frac{5}{9}, \frac{2}{3}, \frac{7}{9}, \frac{5}{9}, \frac{4}{9}, \frac{7}{9}, \frac{8}{9}, \frac{4}{3}, \frac{1}{3}, \frac{2}{9}, \frac{5}{9}, \frac{7}{9}, \frac{5}{9}, \frac{4}{9}, \frac{2}{9}$

5. Insects were captured and measured in a field. The following data show their lengths, in inches:
$\frac{1}{10}, \frac{2}{5}, \frac{3}{10}, \frac{1}{10}, \frac{3}{10}, \frac{1}{2}, \frac{2}{5}, \frac{7}{10}, \frac{1}{10}, \frac{2}{5}, \frac{3}{10}, \frac{1}{5}, \frac{2}{5}, \frac{1}{2}, \frac{3}{10}$

LEARN

Line Plots (B)

Use Line Plots with Fraction Data

You can use operations on the values presented in a line plot to answer questions about the data set.

PROBLEM 1 A machine operator in a factory is trying to adjust a machine to make sure the machine is making parts that are the correct weight. She has collected the weights, in ounces, and has placed them on the line plot.

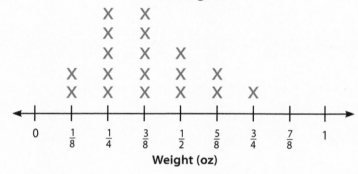

Part Weights

Weight (oz)

QUESTION 1: What is the difference between the greatest value and the least value in the data set?

SOLUTION

1 Identify the least and greatest values in the data set.

least: $\frac{1}{8}$ greatest: $\frac{3}{4}$

2 Find the difference by subtracting. To subtract fractions, the denominators must be the same. Since $\frac{3}{4}$ is equivalent to $\frac{6}{8}$, use $\frac{6}{8}$ instead of $\frac{3}{4}$ when subtracting.

$$\frac{3}{4} - \frac{1}{8} = \frac{6}{8} - \frac{1}{8} = \frac{5}{8}$$

Since the numerator, 5, and the denominator, 8, have no common factors, this answer is already in simplest form.

ANSWER $\frac{5}{8}$ oz

LEARN

QUESTION 2: What is the sum of the two least weights?

SOLUTION The two least weights are $\frac{1}{8}$ and $\frac{1}{8}$. Add and simplify.

$$\frac{1}{8} + \frac{1}{8} = \frac{2}{8}$$

$$\frac{2 \div 2}{8 \div 2} = \frac{1}{4}$$

ANSWER $\frac{1}{4}$ oz

QUESTION 3: What is the sum of all the weights at the value of $\frac{3}{8}$?

SOLUTION Count the number of measurements at $\frac{3}{8}$. There are 5 measurements of $\frac{3}{8}$, so the sum of these is $\frac{3}{8} + \frac{3}{8} + \frac{3}{8} + \frac{3}{8} + \frac{3}{8} = \frac{15}{8}$

You could also find the answer by multiplying the 5 weights of $\frac{3}{8}$.

$$5 \cdot \frac{3}{8} = \frac{5}{1} \cdot \frac{3}{8} = \frac{15}{8}$$

ANSWER $\frac{15}{8}$ oz

QUESTION 4: How many of the weights are at the value of $\frac{5}{8}$ oz or more?

SOLUTION There are 2 measurements of $\frac{5}{8}$ and 1 measurement of $\frac{3}{4}$.

ANSWER There are 3 measurements at $\frac{5}{8}$ oz or greater.

QUESTION 5: What fraction of the total number of weights are at the value of $\frac{5}{8}$ or more?

SOLUTION There are 3 measurements at $\frac{5}{8}$ or greater and 18 measurements total.

As a fraction, this is $\dfrac{\text{\# of measurements at } \frac{5}{8} \text{ or greater}}{\text{total \# of measurements}} = \frac{3}{18} = \frac{3 \div 3}{18 \div 3} = \frac{1}{6}$

ANSWER $\frac{1}{6}$

LEARN

PROBLEM 2 The line plot contains different measurements of liquid, in liters, for identical beakers. Find the amount of liquid each beaker would contain if the total amount in all beakers was distributed equally.

Amounts of Liquid in Beakers

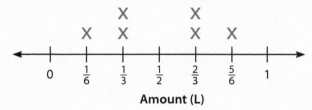

Amount (L)

SOLUTION

1 Since the total amount of liquid is to be distributed equally, calculate the average. Find the total amount of liquid.

$$\frac{1}{6} + \frac{1}{3} + \frac{1}{3} + \frac{2}{3} + \frac{2}{3} + \frac{5}{6}$$
$$= \frac{1}{6} + \frac{2}{6} + \frac{2}{6} + \frac{4}{6} + \frac{4}{6} + \frac{5}{6}$$
$$= \frac{18}{6}$$
$$= 3$$

The total amount of liquid is 3 liters.

2 Since the total amount of liquid now needs to be distributed equally among the beakers, divide the total amount, 3 liters, by the number of beakers, 6.

$$3 \div 6 = \frac{3}{6} = \frac{1}{2}$$

ANSWER To distribute the total amount of liquid equally, each beaker must contain $\frac{1}{2}$ liter of liquid.

For Problems 1–3, answer the following questions:

   (a) What is the difference between the greatest value and the least value in the data set?

   (b) What is the sum of the greatest value and least value in the data set?

   (c) What is the product of the greatest and least value in the data set?

   (d) What fraction of all the values occurs at the least value?

1.

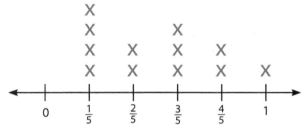

2.

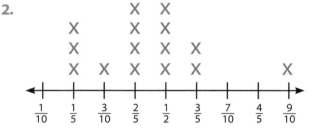

3.

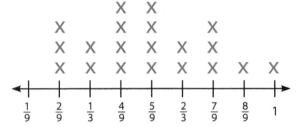

Read the problem and follow the directions.

4. The line plot contains different measurements of liquid in identical beakers. Find the amount of liquid each beaker would contain if the total amount in all beakers was distributed equally.

Amounts of Liquid in Beakers

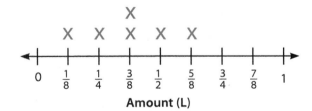

Amount (L)

LEARN

Worked Examples

When you have data to display, use the type of graph that best represents the data. Also be sure that your graph has a title, a scale, axis labels, and if necessary, a legend.

PROBLEM For Arbor Day in 2003, Marcus planted a tree in his backyard. Each year he measures the height of the tree and records the data in his notebook. He has made this line graph to display data he has collected.

2003: 32 inches
2004: 40 inches
2005: 47 inches
2006: 58 inches
2007: 64 inches
2008: 70 inches
2009: 72 inches

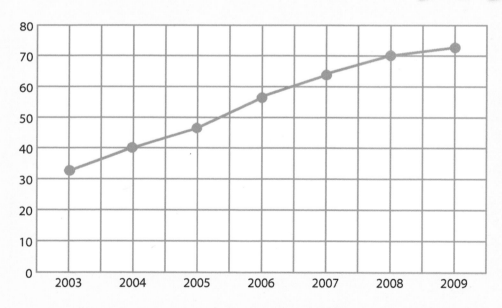

What information is missing from the graph? Fill in the information that is missing. Then explain why the line graph is a good choice for displaying these data.

1 Check to see that the graph has the following parts:
- Title? No
- Scale? Yes
- Axis labels? No
- Legend? You don't need a legend because the graph only has one line.

2 Decide what the vertical axis (*y*-axis) represents. Write a label.

3 Decide what the horizontal axis (*x*-axis) represents. Write a label.

4 Read the problem again. Write a title.

ANSWER The title and labels for the axes are missing. The label for the *y*-axis could be "Height (inches)." The label for the *x*-axis could be "Year." The title for the graph could be "Growth of Marcus's Tree." The line graph is a good choice because it shows change over time.

Read the problem and follow the directions.

1. Tom collected data about the amount of money children charge to wash cars. He wants to compare the amounts that the children charge, so he created the bar graph shown. Fill in the information that is missing from the bar graph. Explain why the bar graph is a good choice for displaying these data.

Name	Amount	Name	Amount	Name	Amount	Name	Amount
Jackson	$10	Shelly	$8	Aislin	$8	Mark	$8
Alice	$8	Ralph	$7	Maggie	$10	Ivy	$3

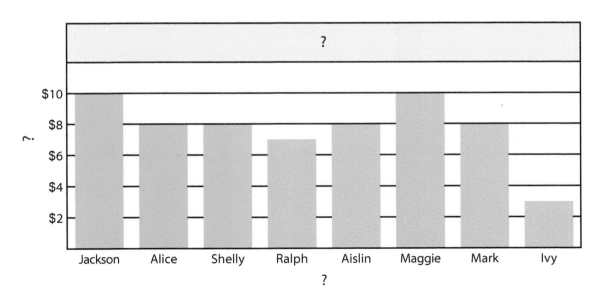

L E A R N

Read the problem and follow the directions.

2. Gregory collected data about the number of sunny days each month for a year.

Month	Number of days
January	17
February	16
March	17
April	18
May	20
June	25
July	27
August	26
September	23
October	20
November	18
December	16

On the next page are three ways to display the data. Which data display do you think best shows the data? Explain your answer.

LEARN

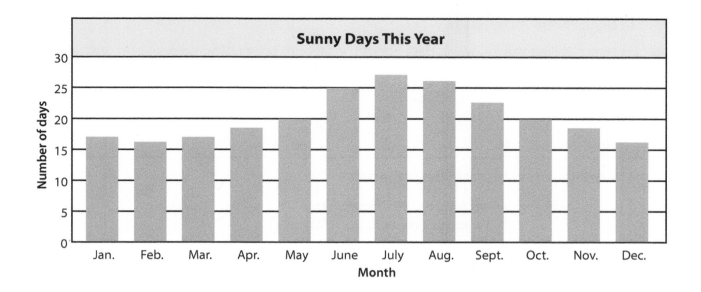

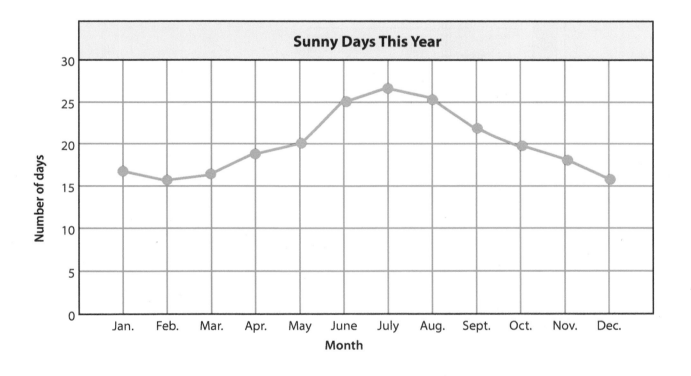

Sunny Days This Year

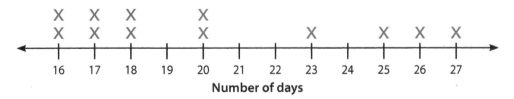

Choose the answer.

3. Louise collected the following data about the favorite colors of some boys and girls.

Color	Number of boys	Number of girls	Color	Number of boys	Number of girls
orange	50	49	green	27	13
purple	34	21	red	3	19

Which data display best represents the data?

A.

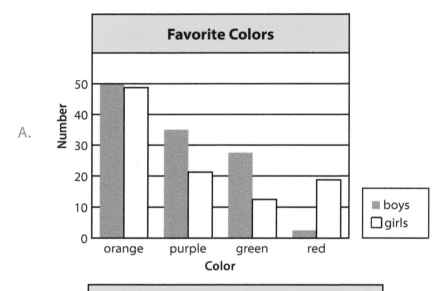

B.

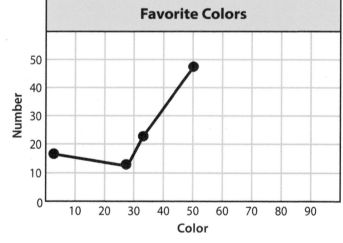

C.

orange	~~卌~~ ~~卌~~ ~~卌~~ ~~卌~~ ~~卌~~ ~~卌~~ ~~卌~~ ~~卌~~ ~~卌~~ ~~卌~~ ~~卌~~ ~~卌~~ ~~卌~~ ~~卌~~ ~~卌~~ ~~卌~~ ~~卌~~ ~~卌~~ ~~卌~~ ||||
purple	~~卌~~ ~~卌~~ ~~卌~~ ~~卌~~ ~~卌~~ ~~卌~~ ~~卌~~ ~~卌~~ ~~卌~~ ~~卌~~ ~~卌~~
green	~~卌~~ ~~卌~~ ~~卌~~ ~~卌~~ ~~卌~~ ~~卌~~ ~~卌~~ ~~卌~~
red	~~卌~~ ~~卌~~ ~~卌~~ ~~卌~~ ||

LEARN

4. Halle collected the following data about the number of miles she ran each day.

Day	Number of miles	Day	Number of miles	Day	Number of miles	Day	Number of miles
Day 1	4	Day 3	4	Day 5	3	Day 7	5
Day 2	6	Day 4	2	Day 6	4		

Which data display best shows the number of miles that occurs most often?

A.

Day 1	||||	Day 5	|||
Day 2	卌 |	Day 6	||||
Day 3	||||	Day 7	卌
Day 4	||		

B.

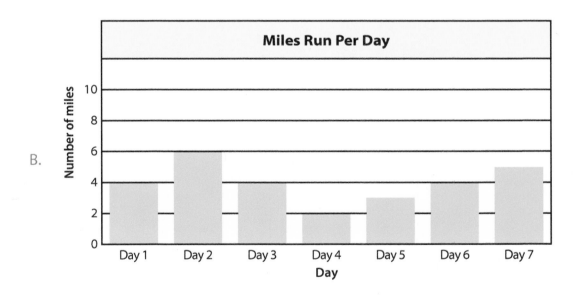

C.

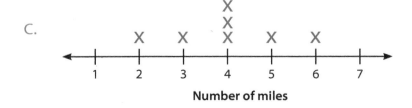

LEARN

Choose the answer.

1. Chelsea collected the following data about the number of days that it rained each month.

Month	Number of Days	Month	Number of Days	Month	Number of Days
January	3	May	6	September	1
February	5	June	3	October	3
March	3	July	0	November	5
April	3	August	2	December	3

Which data display best represents the data?

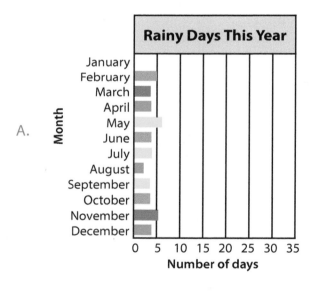

A.

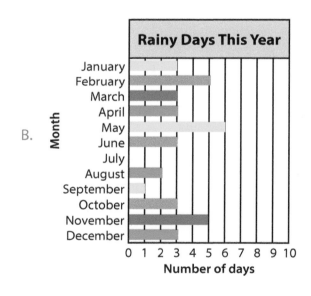

B.

Rainy Days This Year

C.

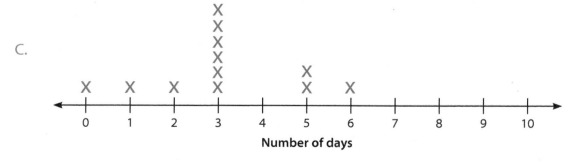

TRY IT

2. Jenelle collected the following data about the number of boys and girls playing different sports.

Sport	Number of boys	Number of girls	Sport	Number of boys	Number of girls
soccer	53	49	ice hockey	27	13
baseball	34	21	field hockey	3	19

Which graph best represents the data?

A.

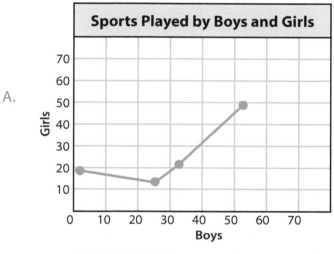

B.

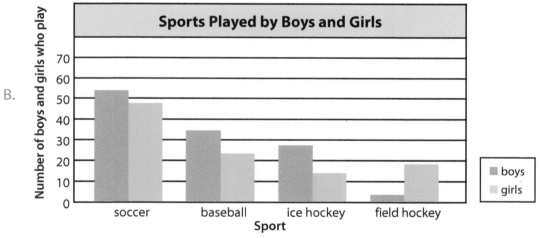

C.

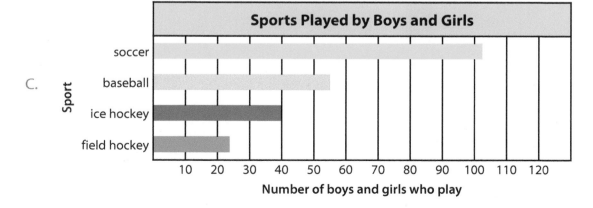

TRY IT

3. Tom collected the following data about the amount other children were charging to wash cars.

Name	Amount	Name	Amount	Name	Amount	Name	Amount
Jackson	$10	Shelly	$8	Aislin	$8	Mark	$8
Alice	$8	Ralph	$7	Maggie	$10	Ivy	$3

Which data display is used to show the amount that occurs most often?

What Other Children Charge to Wash Cars

A.

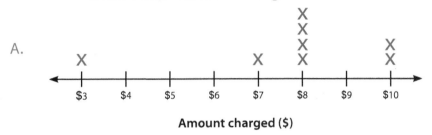

Amount charged ($)

B.

Jackson	卌 卌	Aislin	卌 |||
Alice	卌 |||	Maggie	卌 卌
Shelly	卌 |||	Mark	卌 |||
Ralph	卌 ||	Ivy	|||

TRY IT

4. Kent wanted to know if he would do better on tests if he spent more time studying his notes. Kent collected the following data.

Subject	Time	Score	Subject	Time	Score	Subject	Time	Score
math	30 min	10	math	10 min	5	reading	15 min	7
spelling	15 min	6	math	20 min	7	spelling	15 min	5
math	25 min	8	spelling	25 min	9			

Which data display will best show this information?

A.
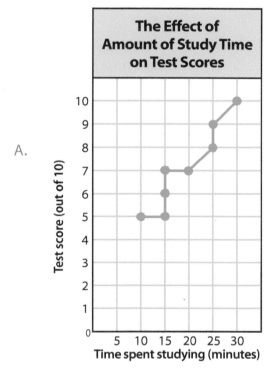

B.
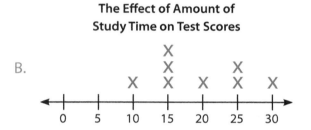

C.
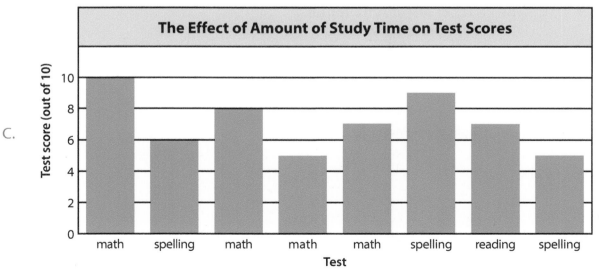

TRY IT

Choose the answer.

5. Gina wanted to know if her sunflowers would grow taller if she gave them more water. Gina collected the following data.

Water	Growth	Water	Growth
10 mL	2 cm	15 mL	4 cm
5 mL	1 cm	10 mL	3 cm
20 mL	5 cm		

Which data display will best show this information?

A.

10 mL of water	$\|\|$
5 mL of water	$\|$
20 mL of water	卌
15 mL of water	$\|\|\|\|$
10 mL of water	$\|\|\|$

B.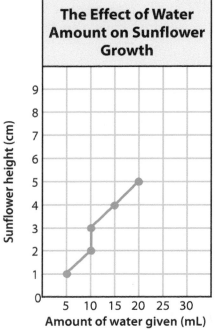

C.

The Effect of Water Amount on Sunflower Growth

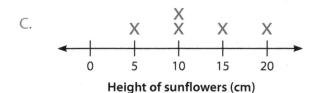

TRY IT

6. State the actions and thinking you used during this lesson as a math learner.

Math Thinking and Actions
I made sense of problems by • Explaining to myself what a problem means and what it asks for • Using drawings or diagrams to represent a problem I was solving
I explained my math thinking clearly.
I tried out new ways to check if an answer is reasonable.
Other

TRY IT